Name _____

Rule When you hear a /k/ sound in a syllable or word, the letters **k, ck,** or **que** will usually stand for that sound.

EXAMPLES

Letters	Word	Sound
k	**k**angaroo	/k/
ck	pi**ck**le	/k/
que	cli**que**	/k/

Directions Circle the letter or letters that stand for the /k/ sound in each word in the box. Then use the words to complete the sentences.

kept	tackle	kick	check
trick	unique	kind	pick
knack	track	key	tickle

1. The football coach was tough, but he was _____ to everyone.

2. He said the _____ to a good team was good players.

3. He was able to _____ players from surrounding schools.

4. He had a _____ for finding talented athletes.

5. He had a _____ way of spotting a team player.

6. Some players had to know how to _____ .

7. Others had to know how to _____ and catch the ball.

8. He taught the players several _____ plays.

9. Players ran around the _____ to get in shape.

10. It would really _____ the coach when he saw a good play.

11. After the game, he _____ going over the plays.

12. This helped the players _____ their own progress.

LESSON 1: Words with the K sound

EXAMPLES		
Letters	**Word**	**Sound**
qu	**qu**een	/kw/
kn	**kn**ee	/n/

Directions Write each word beside its definition.

quest
queen
quarterback
questionnaire
quicksand
quail

1. a female monarch _____

2. a small game bird _____

3. a journey in search of adventure _____

4. the football player who usually calls the plays _____

5. a written form used for gathering information _____

6. loose, wet, deep sand _____

Directions Complete the sentences using the words in the box at the right.

1. Sir Clumsy was not an ordinary _____ .

2. Sir Clumsy was _____ throughout the kingdom.

3. He _____ his name was not complimentary.

4. He was so clumsy, he was on his _____ more than he was on his feet.

5. When he _____ down, he usually fell down.

6. Wherever Sir Clumsy walked, he was sure to _____ something over.

knock
knight
knees
knew
knelt
known

Name _____

EXAMPLES

Letters	Word	Sound
ch	**ch**aracter	/k/
ch	**ch**eap	/ch/
ch	**ch**auffeur	/sh/

Directions Read each pair of sentences. Underline each word in which the letters **ch** stand for the /k/, /ch/, or /sh/ sound. Then circle the sentence that describes the picture.

1. The ship from China anchored near port.
   The captain used a chart to check the ship's course.

2. The orchestra played for the church chorus.
   The audience cheered for the choral group.

3. The parachute hung on a tree branch.
   The pilot reached for the chute's chord.

Directions Complete each sentence with a word from the box.

1. The travel agent gave us a _____ to read.

2. We wanted to _____ the tickets for our trip.

3. We had to _____ our travel plans.

4. I wanted to go to the land of _____ and sunshine.

5. My friend wanted to _____ for sunken treasures.

6. I couldn't wait to _____ some big fish.

catch
orchids
brochure
search
change
purchase

Rule When **c** is followed by **a, o,** or **u,** it usually stands for the /k/ sound. When **c** is followed by **e, i,** or **y,** it usually stands for the /s/ sound.

Directions Read the story, and circle each word with the letter **c.** Then write each word you circled in the correct column. Use each word only once.

A Valuable Harvest

In 1492, Columbus didn't just discover America. He also found that the Native American Indians were cultivating a strange, grasslike plant that today is one of the four most valuable harvests in the entire world—corn.

Of course the Indians had been growing corn for countless decades. Corn played an important part in their everyday life. Indians held ceremonies when placing the seeds in the soil. They used corn patterns to decorate pottery and sculpture.

Early colonists enjoyed juicy ears of corn on the cob and hot, buttered popcorn. Corn was so valuable to the colonists that they often used it as money. People paid their rent, taxes, or debts in corn. They even traded it for marriage licenses!

INDIAN CORN HARVEST.

c sounded as /k/   **c** sounded as /s/

_____   _____   _____

_____   _____   _____

_____   _____   _____

_____   _____   _____

_____   _____

_____   _____

Name _____

Rule When **g** is followed by **a**, **o**, or **u**, it usually stands for the hard sound in **gate**. When **g** is followed by **e**, **i**, or **y**, it usually stands for the soft sound in **gym**.

EXAMPLES

Letter	Word	Sound
g	**g**ame	/g/
g	pa**g**e	/j/

Directions Read each word. Write /**g**/ on the line if the word has the hard sound of **g**. Write /**j**/ on the line if the word has the soft sound of **g**.

1. gymnast _j_
2. gleeful _g_
3. gazebo _g_
4. galloping _g_
5. arrangement _j_
6. gym _j_
7. rage _j_
8. sponge _j_
9. region _j_
10. guess _g_
11. age _j_
12. tragedy _j_

Directions Use the words in the exercise above to solve the crossword puzzle.

Across
4. a disaster or serious event
5. a summerhouse from which a person can gaze at the scenery
6. anger
7. moving very fast
9. an expert in gymnastics
11. number of years a person has lived

Down
1. the way in which something is put together or shown
2. a part of the earth's surface
3. joyful
8. give an estimate
10. something full of holes, used for cleaning

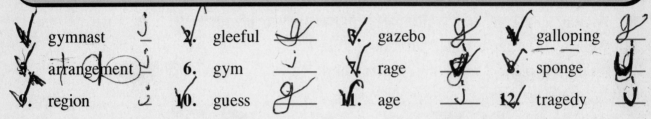

5

LESSON 3: The sounds of G

1. We changed our plans and decided to travel in August.
2. The travel agent helped us look for bargain rates.
3. We went to the travel agency to pick up our tickets.
4. We found our large bags and packed them.
5. At the airport we went to the departure gate.
6. There were many other passengers gathered there.
7. They looked eager and excited to be going on a trip.
8. We sat in the general lounge area and waited to board.
9. We played a game called "It Looks Like."
10. I said the plane looked like a giant bird.

g sounded as /j/   **g** sounded as /g/

_____   _____

_____   _____

_____   _____

_____   _____

_____   _____

_____   _____

_____   _____

Name _____

marketplace	techniques
circle	knows
investigating	mystique
gigantic	questions
archaeologists	unlock

MYSTERY IN STONE

Ghostly giants tower over the Salisbury Plain in England. The huge stones have stood in this spot for over four thousand years—long before even the invention of the wheel.

People have been _____ Stonehenge for centuries, trying to
                                    1
_____ its secrets. _____ are scientists who study
              2   3
ancient times and people. They have tried to find out what_____
                                                                                4
Stonehenge's builders used to move the five-ton stones over one hundred miles to get them
to Stonehenge.

Nobody _____ for sure why Stonehenge was built. Some people
                              5
think it was a temple. Others think Stonehenge may have been a graveyard, a

_____ , or even a _____ calendar!
              6   7

Scientists and scholars from all over the world have been fascinated by the

_____ surrounding these ancient stones, but the few answers that
              8
they find only lead to more _____ . Meanwhile, the great
                                              9
_____ of stones stands silent, casting long shadows across the
              10

empty plain.

_____ dig into the earth to find a clue

_____ study how the stones are put together

_____ stay there overnight with my friends

_____ forget what other scientists have found out

_____ study about the early people who lived on the Salisbury Plain

_____ read about all the legends of Stonehenge

_____   _____
                                    (my idea)

Directions   Now tell how you would solve the Stonehenge mystery. Finish the sentences to explain your technique.

Here's how I plan to solve the mystery of Stonehenge.

First, I'll _____

because _____

Then I'll _____

Finally, if that doesn't work, I'll solve the mystery by _____

_____

Name _____

Rule The letters **f**, **ff**, or **ph** can stand for the /f/ sound.

EXAMPLES

Letters	Word	Sound
ph	dolphin	/f/
f	faster	/f/
ff	scaffold	/f/

Directions Circle the letter or letters that stand for the /f/ sound in each word in the box. Then use the words to complete the sentences.

photographer	famous	nephew	effort
profession	difficult	trophies	beautiful

1. Aunt Rosa's _____ is coming home.

2. He is a well-known _____ for the newspaper.

3. He enjoys working in his _____.

4. His pictures are _____ and interesting.

5. He does his job well in _____ situations.

6. He has been rewarded many times for his care and _____.

7. He has won _____ and other awards for his photographs.

8. Aunt Rosa is proud of her _____ relative.

Directions Read the sentences. Underline the letter or letters that stand for the /f/ sound in each word in boldface print. Then circle the answer to the question.

1. The white cat looked like a **phantom** as it crouched in the corner waiting to leap. What is a **phantom**?

   a wrestler   an elk   a ghost

2. The cat sprang and jumped on the green **philodendron** sitting in the corner. What is a **philodendron**?

   a car   a sweater   a plant

3. The cat **affixed** its claws to the large stalk of the plant. What is **affixed**?

   a tool   a kind of glue   fastened or attached

4. When the cat got hungry it **foraged** for food in the kitchen. What is **foraged**?

   shopped   searched   cooked

9

Rule The consonant **s** can stand for the sound you hear at the beginning of **safe**. Sometimes **s** can stand for the /z/, /sh/, or /zh/ sounds.

EXAMPLES

Letter	Word	Sound
s	sunny	/s/
s	rose	/z/
s	sure	/sh/
s	pleasure	/zh/

Directions Read the words in the box. Listen to the sound of the letter **s** in each word. Then write the words in the correct columns.

pressure	sonata	composer	leisure
several	wise	pleasure	assuring
treasure	sugar	simple	measured
music	sensible	sure	observe

/s/   **/sh/**   **/zh/**   **/z/**

_____ _____ _____ _____

_____ _____ _____ _____

_____ _____ _____ _____

_____ _____ _____ _____

Directions Complete the sentences using words from the box.

1. Beethoven was a great _____.

2. It is a _____ to listen to his music.

3. Beethoven composed _____ even after he became deaf.

4. His works are a great _____.

5. His music is _____ and beautiful.

6. He composed _____ symphonies.

7. You can be _____ that his music will be enjoyed for a long time.

8. Its impact cannot be _____.

Name _____

Rule The letters **wh** can stand for the /h/ sound as in **wh**ole or the /hw/ sound as in **wh**ale.	**EXAMPLES**		
	Letters	Word	Sound
	wh	**wh**ole	/h/
	wh	**wh**ale	/hw/

Directions   Read the article, and circle each word with **wh.** Then write those words in the correct columns below. Write each word only once.

Did you know that the largest kind of animal that has ever lived is swimming somewhere in the earth's oceans? This animal, whose body length can reach 95 feet (29 meters), is the blue whale. This whale is heavier than an elephant and bigger than the largest prehistoric dinosaur we know about.

When scientists study these huge animals, they tell us that they are among the most fascinating animals anywhere on earth.

For example, while these whales have excellent hearing, they have somewhat small ear openings and no real ears at all on the outside of their bodies. These animals who live in the water must breathe air to survive. This means that a blue whale can keep its whole body under water. But it must bring the top of its head to the surface regularly to breathe air.

wh sounded as /h/

wh sounded as /hw/

_____

_____

_____

_____

_____

_____

_____

_____

LESSON 6: The sounds of WH

Rule The letters **sh, ci,** and **ti** can stand for the /sh/ sound.

EXAMPLES

Letters	Word	Sound
sh	**sh**ip	/sh/
ci	spe**ci**al	/sh/
ti	par**ti**al	/sh/

Directions Read each pair of sentences. Underline each word in which you hear the /sh/ sound. Then circle the number of the sentence that describes the picture.

1. We watched the accomplished magician perform wonderful tricks.
2. The audience clapped enthusiastically when the magician finished.

1. Learning to be a computer technician takes special patience.
2. I pushed one button and a message flashed across the screen.

1. The bashful cashier is an accomplished musician.
2. She also appreciates listening to good music.

Directions Complete each sentence with a word from the box.

1. We were watching a _____ program.

2. We saw pictures of the effects of _____ weather.

3. Then a television _____ appeared.

4. We did not _____ having our show interrupted.

5. There would have been _____ time at the end of the program.

harsh
sufficient
commercial
special
appreciate

LESSON 6: Words with the SH sound

Name _____

Directions   Write each word beside its definition. Then write **thin** or **then** to show the sound **th** has in that word.

Rule   The letters **th** can stand for the sound in **thin** or for the sound in **then**.

| thunder | marathon | rhythm |
| threat | weather | enthusiastic |

Definition	**Word**	**Sound of** *thin* **or** *then*
1. eagerly interested	_____	_____
2. a long race or contest	_____	_____
3. condition of atmosphere	_____	_____
4. loud crash	_____	_____
5. intention to hurt	_____	_____
6. recurrence in beat	_____	_____

Directions   Complete each sentence by writing a word from the box at the top of the page.

1. People are _____ about the upcoming concert!

2. A twelve-hour _____ of band music is scheduled.

3. It will be interesting to hear which band has the best _____.

4. The show might be canceled due to rainy _____.

5. There is a _____ of severe storms.

6. We have heard some _____ and have seen lightning.

breathing	healthy	whistled	dish
whimpering	thick	whiskers	who
filthy	shivering	special	patient

1. Tina thought she heard a _____ sound in the bushes.

2. When she looked, she discovered a _____ kitten trying to keep warm.

3. Tina _____ softly to see if the kitten would come to her.

4. Tina felt sorry for the _____ and hungry kitten.

5. She wrapped the kitten in her _____ jacket.

6. She wondered _____ the kitten belonged to.

7. Tina gave the kitten some food and a _____ of milk.

8. She was very _____ and gentle as she cleaned the kitten.

9. The kitten seemed to be _____ but tired.

10. It licked its _____ as it curled up on the floor.

11. Soon, all Tina could hear was its gentle _____.

12. Tina got a basket and made a _____ bed for her new friend.

LESSON 7: Reviewing the sounds of WH, SH, TH

Name _____

Directions   Read the words in the box. Then read the paragraphs below. Write the word from the box that correctly completes each unfinished sentence.

profession	disease	affected	fight	someday
Congressional	what	thousands	leisure	office
enough	meanwhile	effort	throughout	thought
telephone	raised	effective	physicians	observe

Jonas Salk

Jonas Salk was _____
                          1
in New York City. His father was a garment
industry worker, but Jonas dreamed that

_____ he would be part of
        2

the medical _____. He
                    3

put a lot of _____ into his
                  4

schoolwork. In his _____
                            5
time, Jonas worked at part-time jobs to help
pay college expenses.

   Finally, in 1939, Jonas Salk had

completed _____ education
                  6
to graduate from medical school. Instead of

opening a doctor's _____,
                            7
Salk chose to do research on viruses in a
laboratory.

_____ a serious viral
        8

_____ was sweeping the
        9
country. Polio was a disease that

_____ of children between
        10
the ages of four and fifteen contracted. Polio

_____ the nervous system
        11

and could cause a person to lose the ability
to move the arms and legs.

   For several years Salk worked patiently
to develop a polio vaccine. Finally in 1953,
Salk announced that he had found

_____ he had been looking
        12
for—a vaccine that would prevent polio.
Salk, his wife and three children were
among the first volunteers to try the vaccine.
The vaccine was found to be safe. It was then
tested on almost two million schoolchildren

and is now used widely _____
the world.   13

   After years of effort, Jonas Salk was

finally successful in the _____
                                  14
against polio.

15

Write the words from the box on page 15 that correctly answer the questions.

1. In which words do the letters **ph** have the /f/ sound? _____

    _____

2. In which words are the letters **gh** not sounded? _____

    _____   _____

3. In which words do the letters **ff** have the /f/ sound?

    _____   _____   _____   _____

Definition   A **sentence** tells a complete thought or idea. Every sentence needs a subject and a verb. The subject tells who or what the sentence is about. The verb, or action word, tells what the subject is doing.

EXAMPLE

   The Salk vaccine helps prevent polio.

Directions   Think about an invention or discovery you would like to work on. Use some of the words in the box to help answer the questions. Use complete sentences.

unusual	effort	easy	everywhere	symphony
anywhere	might	enough	disease	research

1. What is your idea for an invention or discovery?

    _____

2. What will your invention or discovery do or be used for?

    _____

3. Who are the people who would use and enjoy it?

    _____

4. What tools will you need to work out your idea?

    _____

5. Why did you choose this item to invent or discover?

    _____

   LESSON 8: Review and write

Name _____

EXAMPLES		
Letters	Word	Sound
sc	**sc**ience	/s/
sc	con**sc**ious	/sh/
sc	**sc**amper	/sk/

Directions Circle each word in which the letters **sc** stand for the /sk/ sound. Underline each word in which **sc** stands for the /s/ sound. Draw a box around the word in which **sc** stands for the /sh/ sound.

1. The twins wanted to see the scary science fiction movie.
2. The movie was about a scientist who discovers a long lost tomb.
3. The scent of freshly made popcorn had the twins scrambling to the counter.
4. They got some delicious popcorn before scurrying to their seats.
5. The twins were fascinated by the scene they were watching.
6. The scientist was knocked unconscious by a monster with big muscles.
7. The scowl on the face of the monster scared the viewers.
8. The monster had a long scar on its face.
9. One viewer threw a scarf over his eyes as he screamed.
10. Later the twins tried to describe the movie to their parents.

17

Rule The letters **gn** can stand for the /n/ sound as in **gnat.**

1. The **sovereign** governed the country with wisdom and fairness.
   ○ clown   ○ ruler   ○ traveler

2. The queen's **reign** would last until she died.
   ○ leather strap   ○ water   ○ period of rule

3. The queen was a **benign** ruler who was fair and well liked.
   ○ kindly   ○ cruel   ○ corrupt

4. No one in the country dared to **malign** the queen in front of her loyal followers.
   ○ interrupt   ○ speak badly of   ○ visit

5. The queen started a major **campaign** to improve relationships with other countries.
   ○ a series of actions   ○ a game   ○ a threat

6. Her new **foreign** relations program with other countries was well liked.
   ○ indoors   ○ unfriendly   ○ outside one's country

7. Her loyal advisors **designed** new laws.
   ○ acted upon   ○ thought up   ○ didn't want

8. They presented them for her to **sign.**
   ○ signal   ○ display   ○ write one's name

9. The queen said she would not **resign** unless she could no longer rule.
   ○ give up   ○ initial   ○ go to bed

Directions Use a word in boldface print from the exercise above to complete each of the following sentences.

1. The former governor had to _____ from office due to poor health.

2. Journalists covered the new candidate's _____ for election.

3. Newspapers from _____ countries carried stories about it.

4. The candidate's staff _____ her campaign strategy.

5. The candidate was careful not to _____ her opponent.

6. She said that her _____ as governor would be noted for fairness.

7. She wanted to be known as a _____ governor.

8. Her first act would be to _____ an important and popular bill.

Name _____

Rule The letters **rh** and **wr** can stand for the /r/ sound.

EXAMPLES Letters	Word	Sound
rh	**rh**yme	/r/
wr	**wr**ist	/r/

Directions Read the words below. Underline each word in which you see **rh.** Circle each word in which you see **wr.**

1. rhythm
2. wrote
3. wriggle
4. wrinkled
5. shipwreck
6. rhinoceros
7. wrench
8. rhododendron
9. rheumatism
10. awry
11. writing
12. rhapsody

Directions Use a word from above to complete each sentence.

1. The class _____ a thank-you note to the guide at the zoo.

2. Jeff thanked the guide for showing him the huge _____.

3. Meg enjoyed the _____ of song in the bird building.

4. Matt thought a zebra had _____ since it seemed to limp.

5. All the children liked the _____ skin of the gray elephants.

6. Sandy liked the pink flowers on the _____ plants.

7. Everyone enjoyed watching the snakes _____ and slither in the sand.

8. The teacher agreed that nothing had gone _____ to spoil the day.

9. The teacher mailed the letters after everyone finished _____ them.

LESSON 10: Words with the R sound

Rule The letters **air** and **are** can stand for the /air/ sound.

EXAMPLES

Letters	Word	Sound
are	**care**	/air/
air	h**air**	/air/

Directions Write a word from the box to complete each sentence.

1. Carlos just _____ ahead at his car.

2. He was _____ that the car needed to be repaired.

3. The mechanic told Carlos not to _____ .

4. She said the car could be _____ at the garage.

5. She quoted a _____ price to Carlos.

6. Carlos didn't _____ what it cost.

7. It was a _____ car and worth the money.

8. Carlos said he _____ the car with his brother.

9. He didn't _____ tell his brother about the wreck.

10. The car needed more than a new _____ of tires.

pair
aware
care
shared
stared
fair
despair
dare
repaired
rare

Name _____

Rule The letters **ear** can stand for the /ear/, /air/, or /ur/ sounds.

EXAMPLES

Letters	Word	Sound
ear	cl**ear**	/ear/
ear	p**ear**	/air/
ear	p**ear**l	/ur/

Directions Write the words from the box in the correct column.

yearned	heard	appeared	weary	bear	nearby
clear	swear	research	fear	wearing	searched

year   **pearl**   **pear**

_____   _____   _____

_____   _____   _____

_____   _____   _____

_____   _____   _____

_____

Directions Complete the sentences using words from the box. Each sentence needs two words.

1. We _____ that a wild animal had been spotted _____.

2. We were _____ warm clothing as we _____ the woods in the cold.

3. We became _____ and _____ to rest.

4. Just then we saw what _____ to be _____ tracks.

5. When we took a closer look, it became _____ that we had nothing to _____.

LESSON 11: Sounds EAR can stand for

Directions Complete the crossword puzzle by writing **ear** words that fit the definitions.

Across

2. to gain knowledge
5. hair on the face
6. eager and serious
8. a wheel that has teeth that fit into another wheel
10. listen to
11. ornaments for the ears

Down

1. afraid of nothing
3. close by
4. an animal that is one year old
6. wages or money paid to a person
7. a nickname for someone who is much loved
9. tired

LESSON 11: Reviewing sounds EAR can stand for

Name _____

Directions Complete the sentences using the words with **ild** and **ind** in the box to the right.

1. The _____ blew the leaves off the trees.

2. Darkness made it hard for us to _____ our way.

3. We knew we had to get to the _____ soon.

4. The youngster was _____ and needed help.

5. We didn't _____ that it was raining.

6. The wind was just so _____ and strong.

7. What _____ of trouble was the child in?

8. This case was _____ compared to our last one.

child
mind
wind
wild
find
mild
blind
kind

Directions Complete the sentences using the words with **old** and **ost** in the box to the right.

1. It was rainy and _____ as we searched.

2. We were _____ that the child was in a house.

3. The child was definitely _____ and probably scared.

4. We had to _____ on just a little longer.

5. Suddenly my partner tripped over a wooden _____.

6. Lo and _____, the house was right in front of us.

7. We _____ entered the house and found the child safe.

8. This was by far our _____ rewarding case.

boldly
most
cold
behold
told
post
lost
hold

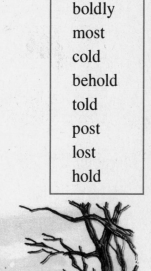

LESSON 12: Words with ILD, IND, OST, OLD

a ghost host	a wild child	a kind mind	sold gold

1. What would you call a brain that thinks of ways to help others?

_____

2. What would you call the creature who invites you to a spooky party?

_____

3. What would you call a young person who misbehaves?

_____

4. What would you call precious metal that someone has bought?

_____

Directions   Write words from the box to complete the sentences.

find	lost	wind	told	mild
sold	most	cold	blinding	gold

1. Kim wanted to buy a _____ pin for her friend Marge before they were

   _____ out.

2. The weather had changed from sunny and _____ to snowy and

   _____ .

3. It was the _____ snow and _____ they had had all winter.

4. Kim's mother worried that she might get _____ in the

   _____ snowstorm.

5. She _____ Kim she would have to _____ another time to go shopping.

Name _____

Directions Read the words in the box. Write one-syllable words in column 1, two-syllable words in column 2, and three-syllable words in column 3.

Hint A word has as many syllables as it has vowel sounds.

disappear	dare	grind	numb	wheat
bold	climber	wholesome	whose	find
unique	questionnaire	meanwhile	cashier	declare
innermost	honeycomb	refreshment	overwhelm	chandelier
		foremost		

One Syllable   **Two Syllables**   **Three Syllables**

_____   _____   _____

_____   _____   _____

_____   _____   _____

_____   _____   _____

_____   _____   _____

_____   _____   _____

Rule   When a single consonant comes between two vowels in a word, the word is usually divided after the consonant if the first vowel is short.

EXAMPLES

mod/el   rob/in

Rule   When a single consonant comes between two vowels in a word, the word is usually divided before the consonant if the first vowel is long.

EXAMPLES

na/ture   ba/con

1. melon ———————————
2. facial ———————————
3. silent ———————————
4. lemon ———————————
5. comic ———————————
6. repair ———————————
7. cabin ———————————
8. benign ———————————
9. declare ———————————
10. visit ———————————
11. pities ———————————
12. modest ———————————
13. design ———————————
14. nasal ———————————
15. music ———————————

16. final ———————————
17. recent ———————————
18. lizard ———————————
19. finish ———————————
20. magic ———————————
21. rotate ———————————
22. petal ———————————
23. pilot ———————————
24. punish ———————————
25. medal ———————————
26. cities ———————————
27. radish ———————————
28. famous ———————————
29. patient ———————————
30. bison ———————————

LESSON 13: Recognizing syllables

Name _____

humankind	they	fearful	grind	holds	earth
scientific	through	most	methods	beneath	ancient

The Mystery of Earthquakes

Earthquakes have happened many times _____ the ages. People have

_____ 1

been both _____ and
2
curious when they felt the earth suddenly

tremble _____ their feet.
3

_____ has always tried
4

to explain and predict this mysterious and terrifying occurrence. For example, the ancient Greeks explained earthquakes by

saying _____ happened
5

because the sea god Poseidon was shattering rocks and shaking the land every time he was angry at a giant named Polybotes.

When scientists first began studying earthquakes, it almost seemed that the

_____ Greeks were right.
6

Scientists found that _____
7

earthquakes *do* happen beneath the ocean. But the cause of earthquakes is not gods battling giants.

Today, scientific _____
8

of earthquake study have brought us new knowledge. We know that earthquakes are caused by unstable sections of rock that shift

and _____ against each
9

other under the earth's surface.

The study of earthquakes has helped scientists find out about the interior of the

_____, but there is much
10

more to learn. Both the timing of future earthquakes and methods for gauging their severity are secrets which the earth still holds.

Directions Now use the words in the box to answer the questions below.

1. Which words have the same **th** sound as the word *thin?* _____,

_____, _____, _____

2. Which word has the same sound of *ear* as the word *clear?* _____

3. Which words rhyme with *behind?* _____, _____

health	overwrought	fearful	weary	kindness	find
search	mother	father	brother	sympathy	careful

Reporter: What was it like when the earthquake hit?

You: _____

_____

Reporter: How have volunteers helped the victims of this crisis?

You: _____

_____

Reporter: What belongings were lost during the quake, and how will the owners go about recovering them?

You: _____

_____

Reporter: Have most of the family members involved been reunited?

You: _____

_____

Proofread your sentences.

Does each sentence begin with a capital letter and end with the correct punctuation? _____

Does each sentence make sense? _____

Name _____

©MCP All Rights Reserved.

Directions Read each sentence. Draw a line under each word that contains the /ā/ sound. Then circle the letters that stand for that sound.

Rule The vowel digraphs **ai** and **ay** can stand for the /ā/ sound you hear in **aim** and **play.**

1. When time is available, I paint a picture for my parents' anniversary.
2. I should explain that I do my painting in a special studio.
3. My studio is filled with pails, trays, and other containers.
4. The floor is stained with paint I used on earlier days.
5. I often stay in my studio for hours, never failing to daydream at my easel.
6. I am working on a picture of a train, whizzing along on the tracks through a field of hay.
7. The last painting I did featured a dainty sailboat traveling across the sea.
8. I hope I will not be detained so I can complete my current project today.

Directions Draw a line under the word in each row that contains the sound /ā/. Then circle the letters that stand for that sound.

1. tramp   tap   tar   tram   tray
2. drab   delay   dance   dabble   damp
3. crayon   cancel   clatter   canister   candle
4. rabid   ran   ranted   remain   remark
5. matches   marches   maybe   match   mat
6. pails   pals   plant   pans   pats
7. watch   arrest   answer   argue   anyway
8. drama   daydream   dam   dad   dare
9. prance   planter   payment   padlock   pantry
10. hatch   half   harvest   haystack   hall

29

Directions Complete each sentence with a word from the box.

train	away	remained	delay
rain	sway	explained	pails
repay	stay	pain	relay
grains	raisin	sailing	sprained

1. We had fun when we were _____ on vacation.

2. Traveling by _____ , we departed from our home in Phoenix, Arizona.

3. For a week, we _____ at our aunt and uncle's home in California.

4. We woke early each morning and left their house without _____ .

5. Aunt Flo and Uncle George took us _____ on the ocean.

6. The weather was in our favor, since it did not _____ once.

7. Aunt Flo gave us our life jackets and _____ how to use them.

8. We enjoyed the moments when the boat would _____ in the breeze.

9. On the shore, we built sandcastles with our shovels and _____ .

10. In the evenings, we played games and held _____ races.

11. During one race, Uncle George tripped and _____ his ankle.

12. Uncle George insisted that his injury did not cause him much _____ .

13. We thought about how we could _____ them for the good time we had.

14. As a thank-you present, we baked several loaves of _____ bread.

15. We added nuts and several types of _____ to the batter.

16. We were sorry when our _____ had reached its end.

LESSON 15: Vowel digraphs AI, AY

Name _____

Rule The vowel digraphs **ee** and **ei** can stand for the /ē/ sound.

EXAMPLES

Letters	Word	Sound
ee	s**ee**	/ē/
ei	s**ei**ze	/ē/

Directions Read each word and circle the letters that stand for the /ē/ sound. Then write each word in the correct column below.

needle	deceitful	receipt	Sheila
conceited	wheelbarrow	keeper	receiver
agreement	ceiling	steeple	greenhouse
beetle	succeed	protein	sleep

see   **seize**

_____   _____

_____   _____

_____   _____

_____   _____

_____   _____

_____   _____

_____

1. Sheila Franklin owns and operates a greenhouse in her community.

2. She has agreed never to move it from its location on a quiet and secluded street.

3. She enjoys the sight of strong trees, flowering plants, and young seedlings.

4. The sides and ceiling of the greenhouse are glass, which Sheila keeps shiny.

5. Outside, an enormous weeping willow sweeps over the sprawling property.

6. Beside it, a beech tree, with gray wood and edible nuts, is visible.

7. Sheila cultivates honey from beehives she keeps on her property.

8. She succeeds in her business because she is deeply devoted to her job.

9. One can often see her hauling soil and fertilizer in a large wheelbarrow.

10. She is always ready to seize each day and never seems to get sleepy!

11. She reminds her customers to keep their receipts, since she guarantees each plant.

12. Being neither conceited nor deceitful, Sheila receives many compliments from patrons.

LESSON 16: Vowel digraphs EE, EI

Name _____

Directions Read each sentence. Draw a line under each word that has the /ō/ sound. Then circle the letters that stand for that sound.

Rule The vowel digraphs **oa, oe,** and **ow** can stand for the ō sound you hear in **coat, toe,** and **row.**

1. Luis, a person I know, is certain that he will grow taller during the next few years.
2. He boasts that he will one day be as tall as his favorite basketball players.
3. Luis's abilities show that he is the best basketball player on our team.
4. Luis bounces the ball and stands on tiptoe when he makes free throws.
5. A talented athlete, he shows good sportsmanship wherever he goes.
6. If he misses a shot or commits a foul, Luis never moans and groans.
7. Even when he outscores every other player, Luis does not brag and gloat.
8. Promising never to outgrow his school spirit, he wears our school crest on his coat.

Directions Complete each sentence with a word from the box.

1. In our home economics class today, we baked _____ of bread.

2. I forgot to bring my copy of the recipe, so I had to

   _____ Joan's.

3. We carefully combined the ingredients in large mixing

   _____.

4. Tomorrow, we will _____ the bread and prepare a breakfast.

5. We will serve the toast with _____ eggs and grapefruit juice.

6. We will poach the eggs in a _____ pan.

7. If time allows, Mrs. Harris will also let us make _____.

8. Before the class _____ on to the next unit, we will have a test.

borrow
shallow
loaves
toast
goes
oatmeal
poached
bowls

Eighteen words in which the vowel digraphs **oa, oe,** and **ow** have the /ō/ sound are hidden in the puzzle. Some go across, and others go up and down. Circle each word as you find it in the puzzle, then write the word in the correct column.

```
S C A R E C R O W L A I S O W
H F M A N X F O E C L O A D I
O I T T H R O W T D O E Z Y S
W R O O S T P E L M M O A N G
B C S R Y B E F O B L R E N T
T E L O D E T O A D S T O O L
O T O W C C A A Y F A N T Y B
M M A T O E L N A O B F L O A
O R N A C U T A N A T I N R O
R D R O O X R B T M S O A K F
R F E Z A A T H E L T O O M B
O T L C B R T O A C D B T K L
W M O P C L P E E F H J N O R
```

oa   **ow**

_____   _____

_____   _____

_____   _____   **oe**

_____   _____   _____

_____   _____   _____

_____   _____   _____

_____   _____   _____

Use a word you found in the puzzle to complete each sentence below.

1. After ice skating in the cold, we drank hot _____ to help warm us.

2. _____ we will row the boat on the lake.

LESSON 17: Vowel digraphs OA, OE, OW

Name _____

Life in Colonial America

Life was not easy for the people who came to the coast of North America in colonial d_____s. But they were determined to st_____, and they worked hard to succ_____d. One of the m_____n occupations was farming. Many colonial families m_____nt_____ned their _____n small farms where they r_____sed livestock, gr_____n, and other crops. The rocky terr_____n and harsh weather made it difficult for the farmers to gr_____ more than they needed to f_____d themselves.

In other parts of New England, people earned their living in different w_____s. Along the coast, fishing was important to many colonists. B_____t building was also important to the c_____stal area, and many people cla_____med that ships

built there were the best afl_____t. Lumber for these ships came from nearby forests of _____ks and evergr_____ns.

Other colonists worked as storek_____pers and merchants. They bought local products and sent them to Europe. The money they rec_____ved for these goods was used as p_____ment for things they knew their fellow colonists would buy—such as sugar, molasses, clothes, hammers, n_____ls, and h_____s. As the merchants became more successful, the small towns grew, and soon the colonial areas b_____sted several important cities.

BUILDING HOUSES AT PLYMOUTH.

35

What do good writers look for when they revise their work? One of the first things they do is check to see that each sentence in the paragraph tells about the same idea.

Directions Read the paragraph below and find the sentence that does not tell about the same idea as the other sentences. Draw a line through that sentence.

One of the main occupations in colonial North America was farming. Many colonial families lived and worked on their own small farms. The soil was rocky, and the weather was harsh. Fishing and shipbuilding provided jobs for those who lived along the Atlantic coast. The farmers usually could grow only enough to feed themselves.

You probably noticed that four of the five sentences in the paragraph are about farming in colonial North America. The fourth sentence, however, is about fishing and shipbuilding. It does not belong in this paragraph.

Directions Now read the paragraph below. Find the sentences that do not tell about the same idea as the other sentences. Draw a line through them. Then rewrite the paragraph, leaving out the sentences that do not belong.

Boat building was also important, and many colonists worked building ships. North American merchants sent local products to England. When the merchant ships returned, they carried the goods needed by the colonists. Fishing was one of the most important occupations in coastal towns. The lively trade kept up by these merchants helped keep the colonies supplied with sugar, clothing, and tools. The merchants and storekeepers were important to the growth of the small towns into cities.

_____

_____

_____

_____

_____

_____

_____

LESSON 18: Review and write

Rule The vowel digraph ea can stand for the /ā/ sound, the /e/ sound, or the /ē/ sound.

EXAMPLES

Letters	Word	Sound
ea	br**ea**k	/ā/
ea	h**ea**d	/e/
ea	l**ea**f	/ē/

Directions Read each sentence. Underline the words in each sentence that contain the double vowel **ea.** Then write the word in the correct column.

1. Richard, Carlos, and Mark will depart for the music festival tomorrow at daybreak.
2. After a breakfast of wheat toast and milk, they will leave for the outdoor festival.
3. The popular festival will be held at the beach near the breakwater.
4. The boys are eager to see their favorite rock stars perform exciting feats.
5. Richard is looking forward to seeing a new band called T-Bone and the Great Steaks.
6. He hopes that the band will perform some elaborate break dancing routines.
7. Carlos plans to wear his favorite T-shirt underneath a heavy sweater.
8. At the festival, Mark hopes they will find seats close to the stage.
9. Carlos says that sitting too close could pose a threat to their health.
10. The boys are sure that the festival will provide them with treasured memories.

break /ā/	**head /e/**	**leaf /ē/**
_____	_____	_____
_____	_____	_____
_____	_____	_____
_____	_____	_____
_____	_____	_____
	_____	

1. "It's my _____," I told Jan, "to help you with your laundry."

2. I held the basket as Jan _____ in and removed the clothes.

3. She dropped the clothes into the washing machine and added

   _____.

4. Turning to _____ the laundry room, I saw a sock on the floor.

5. I picked it up and pulled off a loose _____ that hung from the sock.

6. We took a short _____ before we tackled our next chore.

7. Jan held the bucket _____ as I filled it with hot water.

8. "Are you _____?" she asked, as I shut off the water.

9. Vigorously, we scrubbed the floor _____ the table.

10. "We've worked so hard," I panted, "we deserve a _____ dinner!"

reached
steak
beneath
pleasure
steady
leave
thread
break
ready
bleach

ea sounded as /ā/   **ea** sounded as /e/   **ea** sounded as /ē/

_____ _____ _____

_____ _____ _____

           _____ _____

           _____ _____

Name _____

Directions Read each sentence. Draw a line under each word with a vowel digraph **ei** or **ey** that stands for the /ā/ sound. Circle the letters that stand for the /ā/ sound.

Rule The vowel digraphs **ei** and **ey** can stand for the /ā/ sound.

1. Suli held tightly to the reins as he guided his horse along the path.

2. The narrow path, which was littered with rocks, sprawled for eight miles.

3. Suli glanced ahead to survey the surrounding terrain.

4. To the west, he could see freight trains traveling on tracks.

5. To the east, a thin veil of fog hung over the town of Peyton.

6. Nervously, he watched a bird overhead, circling its prey.

7. His spirits soared as he saw a reindeer peering around a tree.

8. As his horse increased its pace, Suli tugged on the reins, crying, "Hey, Fleetfoot, slow down!"

9. With determination, Suli held his ground, and Fleetfoot obeyed him.

10. A feeling of relief spread over Suli as he finally spotted his neighbor's house.

Directions Reach each word listed below. Circle the letters that stand for the /ā/ sound. Then write the number of the word on the line in front of its definition.

1. vein _____ to do what one is told or asked

2. obey _____ to look over carefully

3. rein _____ a blood vessel that carries blood back to the heart

4. survey _____ a strap of leather used to control a horse

Rule The vowel digraphs au and aw stand for the same sound.	**EXAMPLES**		
	Letters	Word	Sound
	au	**Au**gust	/aw/
	aw	dr**aw**	/aw/

Directions Complete each sentence with a word from the box.

autumn	scrawl	author	draw	autographs	awfully	cautiously	drawers

1. Every _____, the school yearbook staff begins its work.

2. Working _____ hard, the student photographers take pictures.

3. At all school functions, they _____ wait for great shots.

4. When the photographs are developed, they are stored in _____.

5. Every year, an _____ is chosen to write an essay for the yearbook.

6. An artistic student is selected to _____ the yearbook's cover.

7. When the books are distributed, everyone eagerly requests _____.

8. The students willingly _____ messages in each other's books.

Directions Write the number of each word on the line beside its meaning.

1. shawl   _____ a small, round, shallow dish

2. cautious   _____ to melt; to become unfrozen

3. applaud   _____ not graceful; clumsy

4. thaw   _____ to express approval by clapping hands

5. awkward   _____ a large pot or kettle

6. saucer   _____ bite, chew, or wear away

7. withdraw   _____ to use up completely

8. gnaw   _____ a cloth worn as a covering for the shoulders

9. cauldron   _____ very careful

10. exhaust   _____ to take or pull out

LESSON 20: Vowel digraphs AU, AW

Name _____

Directions Read the words in the box. Then write the word that names each picture.

chief	tie	shield
pie	thief	field

1.

_____

2.

_____

3.

_____

4.

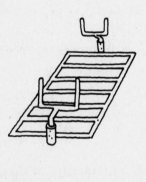

_____

5.

_____

6.

_____

Directions In each word you wrote above, circle the letters that stand for the vowel sound. Now use the words to complete the rule below.

The vowel digraph **ie** can stand for the long _____ sound you hear in the words _____ , _____ , _____ , and _____ . It can also stand for the long _____ sound you hear in the words _____ and _____ .

| relief | untie | diet | pieces | shrieked | grief |
| brief | achieve | tried | disbelief | thief | believed |

1. The pet club held its _____ weekly meeting after school.

2. Jason announced that his dog, Trooper, was misbehaving and giving him

   _____ .

3. At first, Mr. Andrews, the club sponsor, shook his head in _____ .

4. Jason explained that Trooper was a _____ since he stole dog treats from a kitchen cabinet.

5. He added, "Trooper always tries to _____ my shoelaces, too!"

6. The club members _____ with laughter as they imagined Trooper in action.

7. Then everybody _____ to offer solutions to Jason's problem.

8. "How might Jason _____ success in dealing with his dog?" asked Mr. Andrews.

9. Annie said she _____ that the dog was seeking attention.

10. "You might want to talk to your veterinarian," said Paul, "to see if Trooper's

    _____ should be changed."

11. Steven asked Jason, "Why don't you reward Trooper with small

    _____ of treats?"

12. With a sigh of _____ , Jason thanked the club members for their help.

Name _____

Directions The words in the box have letters and sounds that you studied in this unit. Read the words. Then read the paragraphs below. Choose the correct word from the list to complete each unfinished sentence. You may use your dictionary.

heyday	saw	dissatisfied	tried
automatically	toiled	countries	already
factories	Northeast	brief	overseas
awful	stream	cause	thread
great	spread	they	least

People who lived in America during the first half of the 1800s _____ 1 major changes in their way of life. One _____ 2 of these _____ 3 changes was the use of machinery to make things that once had been made only by human hands. Factories first appeared in the _____ 4 in New England. At first, cloth and _____ 5 had been made by hand by people who worked in their own homes. Then spinning and weaving machines were developed that could make these products almost _____ 6.

The first American textile plant was built in Pawtucket, Rhode Island, near a river that provided water power for the machines. Soon _____ 7 and machines _____ 8 across the country until it seemed that there was a factory beside every river and _____ 9. The _____ 10 of machines had begun!

Where did the workers for these factories come from? Some were in New England _____ 11 working on small, poor farms. Other workers came from other _____ 12.

Life in the factories could be _____ 13 at times. Men, women, and children might work 18 hours a day, 6 days a week. Often they were paid less than $2 a week. For these people, factory life was hard, and many were _____ 14 enough to leave. Others decided that factory life was not worse than what _____ 15 had had before, and they stayed.

Definition Sequence is the order in which things happen. Always put details in the correct sequence.

A. ____ The factories that came to New England completely changed this.

B. ____ With the factories came spinning and weaving machines.

C. ____ When people used machines instead of their hands, they could produce ten times as much cloth as before.

D. ____ Until the 1800s, people made cloth and thread by hand, working in their own homes.

Directions Write a paragraph by writing the sentences in the correct order on the lines below. Then add a fifth sentence to complete the paragraph.

_____

_____

_____

_____

_____

_____

_____

_____

_____

_____

_____

_____

_____

_____

Name _____

Rule The vowel digraph **oo** stands for the vowel sound in **too** and the vowel sound in **look**.

EXAMPLES		
Letters	Word	Sound
oo	m**oo**n	/o͞o/
oo	b**oo**k	/oo/

Directions Write the correct name for each picture. Then circle the letters that stand for the vowel sound that you hear in that name.

1.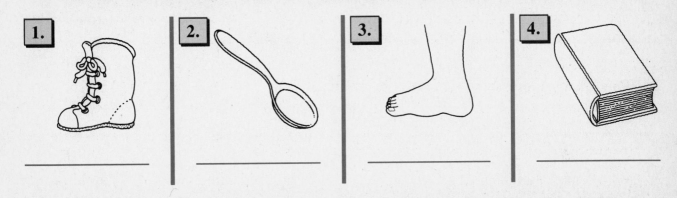
_____

2.
_____

3.
_____

4.
_____

Directions Read the poem. Circle each word that contains the vowel digraph **oo.** Then write each word you circled in the correct column. Use each word only once.

Nosey the snoopy rooster
And Ray the laughing baboon
Took off on a flight
Last Monday night
In Ray's wooden balloon.
Right through a typhoon
They sailed until noon,
But soon they came down with a swoop.
"Look, you can't fly all day,"
Said Nosey to Ray,
"When you've got termites
In your balloon!"

oo as in **boot**   **oo** as in **book**

_____   _____   _____

_____   _____   _____

_____   _____   _____

_____   _____   _____

LESSON 23: Vowel digraph OO

EXAMPLES

Letters	Word	Sound
oo	m**oo**n	/oo̅/
oo	c**oo**k	/oo/
oo	fl**oo**d	/ŭ/

Directions Circle the word that completes each sentence, and write it on the line.

1. We are planning our special _____ picnic.

   classroom
   foolish
   woodwork

2. Tony, our class president, writes our plans in his

   _____ .

   checkbook
   notebook
   bookshelf

3. Ms. O'Rourke announces a _____ plan for the picnic's success.

   foolish
   foolproof
   driftwood

4. She assigns each _____ a specific responsibility.

   schoolchild
   footprint
   bloodhound

5. The class decides to have the picnic near the _____ .

   cook
   look
   brook

6. It is located in a beautiful _____ area near the school.

   wooded
   cooked
   looked

7. "All the shady trees will keep us _____ ," says Tony.

   fool
   pool
   cool

8. It will be easy for our class to _____ to the picnic area.

   troop
   hoop
   pool

Name _____

Directions Write **i** beside each word that has the /i/ sound you hear in *built*. Write **oo** beside each word that has the /ōō/ sound you hear in *fruit*.

Rule The vowel digraph **ui** can stand for the /i/ sound in **built** or the /ōō/ sound in **fruit**.

1. _____ cruise

2. _____ build

3. _____ guilty

4. _____ guitar

5. _____ suit

6. _____ juice

7. _____ building

8. _____ bruise

9. _____ pursuit

10. _____ recruit

11. _____ nuisance

12. _____ biscuits

Directions Complete each sentence with a word from the box.

| recruit | built | suit | fruits | guitar |

1. The museum has _____ a special room for exhibiting its folk art.

2. There is an elaborately carved _____ there, along with several other musical instruments.

3. On the wall there is an unusual painting of a man wearing a purple

_____ .

4. Another display features carved wooden objects such as _____ and other shapes.

5. The museum is hoping to _____ volunteers to conduct tours.

47

1. My parents went on a _____ to Saint Thomas.

    bruise ○   cruise ○   fruit ○

2. They stayed in a hotel that had been _____ a century ago.

    cruised ○   built ○   guilt ○

3. During the day, their favorite _____ was taking long walks.

    pursuit ○   recruit ○   built ○

4. The hot Caribbean weather was _____ for being outdoors.

    suitable ○   suite ○   suits ○

5. They walked the crowded streets, often buying _____ from sidewalk vendors.

    guilt ○   fruit ○   cruise ○

6. My mother said the fruit was always _____ and delicious.

    juicy ○   guilty ○   built ○

7. She never once saw a _____ on a banana!

    bruise ○   cruise ○   fruit ○

8. They liked to stop at an outdoor restaurant that served wonderful _____.

    suits ○   biscuits ○   cruises ○

9. My father enjoyed watching street musicians playing _____ and steel drums.

    guitars ○   suits ○   juice ○

10. They said they felt _____ having so much fun without me.

    rebuilt ○   guilders ○   guilty ○

11. I hope I don't make a _____ of myself for asking so many questions about their trip!

    recruit ○   nuisance ○   suited ○

LESSON 24: Vowel digraph UI

Name _____

> **Directions** Read the words in the box. Then read the paragraphs below. Write the word from the box that correctly completes each unfinished sentence.

build	foolish	Soon	goods
floods	fruits	took	built

FROM THE LAKES TO THE HUDSON.—A GRAIN-BOAT ON THE ERIE CANAL.—SKETCHED BY JOSEPH BECKER.

The Erie Canal

Have you ever seen a canal? A canal is a channel filled with water through which large ships can travel. During the early 1800s, canals were very important. They linked together many American cities, making it possible for boats to carry farm products and manufactured

_____ back and forth across
1
the land.

The Erie Canal was one of the earliest and most important waterways to be

_____. It joined the Hudson
2
River in eastern New York State with the city of Buffalo on Lake Erie. This canal helped link New York City and the Great Lakes.

Work on the Erie Canal began in 1817. Thousands of workers were needed for the job of digging the "big ditch," as it was called. The laborers endured sickness,

hunger, and even _____. It
3

_____ eight years and seven
4

million dollars to _____ the
5
canal. When it was finished in 1825, there was a channel 363 miles (594 km) long and 4 feet deep. It was wide enough for several boats to pass at the same time.

How successful was the canal? Had it

been _____ to spend so much
6
time, money, and effort on a big ditch? When the canal was finished, the cost of shipping goods between New York City and Buffalo fell from $100 to just $10 per ton. Over 13,000 trips were made through the canal

in its first year alone. _____
7

farm products of all kinds—meat, grain,

_____, vegetables—were
8
traveling eastward and westward faster than before.

49

When you look over what you have written, ask yourself these questions:

1. Have I used words that *help* the reader understand what I am trying to say?

2. Have I given interesting details that help the reader see what is being described?

3. Have I used colorful words that will make what I have written *interesting* and *exciting*?

Directions Read each pair of sentences. Circle the number of the sentence that is more interesting and gives a better picture.

1. Many workers were needed for the job of digging the canal.
2. Thousands of workers were needed for the job of digging this "big ditch" across New York State.

1. When finished, the canal was long and wide and a few feet deep.
2. The Erie Canal measured 363 miles long and four feet deep when it was finished in 1825.

Did you notice that in both examples, the second sentence contains more details to help the reader form a better picture of what is being described?

Directions Revise the paragraph. Use details from the article on page 49 to make the paragraph more interesting.

It took several years and much money to build the canal. The people who did the work endured many hardships. But the canal was worth the effort. It cost less money to ship goods. Many trips were made through the canal.

_____

_____

_____

_____

_____

_____

_____

LESSON 25: Review and write

Name _____

Directions Complete each sentence with a word from the box.

1. Jack said he would _____ helping with the gardening.

2. Wearing _____ overalls, he walked out to the yard.

3. Jack kneeled down to touch the _____.

4. It was still _____ from an earlier rainfall.

5. He noticed that birds had nearly _____ some flowers.

6. As he saw a large, squirming insect, Jack _____ in disgust.

7. Swiftly, he moved his hand to _____ it.

8. Jack enjoys his work and was _____ when it began to rain.

soil
disappointed
destroyed
enjoy
corduroy
avoid
recoiled
moist

Directions In the puzzle, circle eight words containing the diphthongs **oi** and **oy**. Then write the words on the lines at the right.

B M I O S T O Y   _____

O L T P O I N T   _____

Y T A M I Y M B   _____

A E N B L U R P   _____

L T O I L R E O   _____

A J I L M H D I   _____

W O S O I Y E L   _____

R I E O U A N E   _____

A N A B I D T Z

51

Directions Write the letter of each definition beside the word that goes with it. Then circle the diphthong in each word.

—— **1.** r e c o i l e d

—— **2.** e n j o y s

—— **3.** t u r m o i l

—— **4.** t o i l

—— **5.** d i s a p p o i n t

—— **6.** d e s t r o y e d

—— **7.** a v o i d

—— **8.** a n n o y e d

A. hard, tiring work

B. ruined; put an end to; broke in pieces

C. to fail to satisfy someone's wishes

D. to keep away from; not see or use

E. drew or shrank back in dislike or fear

F. to get pleasure from

G. irritated; bothered

H. noise; disturbance, commotion

Directions Now use one of the words from above to complete each of the following sentences.

1. Betty usually ——————— her job at the clothing store.

2. Today, she almost ——————— as she entered the store.

3. With the big sale going on, the store was in ———————.

4. Betty walked up and down the aisles, trying to ——————— the crowds.

5. The shoppers soon ——————— the displays Betty had worked so hard to create.

6. Feeling ———————, Betty went to speak to Carol, her supervisor.

7. "Betty," Carol cried, "I have some news that won't ——————— you!"

8. "All your ——————— has earned you a promotion to assistant manager!"

LESSON 26: Diphthongs OI, OY

Directions Read the words in each row. Underline the words that contain the same vowel sound. Then circle the letters that stand for that sound.

Hint The diphthongs **ou** and **ow** often stand for the vowel sound you hear in **loud** and **down**.

1.	growl	grunt	ground
2.	droop	drowsy	doubtful
3.	outbreak	floodlight	flower
4.	funny	power	foundation
5.	counter	prowl	prune
6.	unstable	eyebrow	compound
7.	mountainous	cow	explode
8.	scramble	slouch	downstream
9.	township	mouthful	tawny
10.	outweigh	rowdy	rusting
11.	account	coward	corner
12.	short	shower	shout

Directions Use a phrase from the box to answer each question. Then circle the letters that make the **ou** or **ow** vowel sound in each word.

sound pound	sour power	now chow	fowl towel	brown gown

1. What would you call a cloth to wipe off a chicken?

   _____

2. What would you call sixteen ounces of noise?

   _____

3. What would you call the most up-to-date food?

   _____

4. What slogan could you use to advertise lemons?

   _____

5. What would you call a dirty dress?

   _____

1. The weather was dreary, and it rained ———————— the day.

   about
   throughout
   outweigh

2. Dennis and Aimee felt tired and ————————.

   drowsy
   soundly
   hound

3. In poor spirits, they ———————— wearily on the sofa.

   pouched
   couched
   slouched

4. "What can we do to perk up?" Dennis wondered ————————.

   aloud
   proud
   shroud

5. "Let's dress as ———————— and have a circus!" said Aimee.

   crowns
   clowns
   sours

6. Dennis ———————— with laughter at the idea.

   howled
   glowered
   prowled

7. "I can wear my trick ———————— that sprays water," he said.

   power
   vowed
   flower

8. "And I'll wear that funny green wig you ————————."

   wound
   found
   rowdy

9. She added, "We can paint wide smiles around our ————————."

   mouths
   fouls
   towels

LESSON 27: Diphthongs OU, OW

Name _____

Directions Complete each sentence with a word from the box.

crew	drew	strewn	renew
few	jewelry	jewels	nephew
shrewd	new	pewter	newspaper

1. Ron Richter is known in town as a _____ businessperson.

2. He owns a _____ shop.

3. His _____, Calvin, works in the store each weekend.

4. Ron also employs a _____ other workers.

5. Ron takes great pride in this dedicated _____ of workers.

6. The shop is filled with gold, silver, and _____ objects.

7. In the front windows, gems and _____ sparkle and shine.

8. Gleaming watches, bracelets, and rings are _____ in glass cases.

9. Each Sunday, Ron advertises his special sales in

    the _____.

10. Last Sunday's advertisements _____ large crowds to the shop.

11. If business continues to boom, Ron might not _____ the lease on his shop.

12. In fact, he might be able to move to a _____, bigger shop.

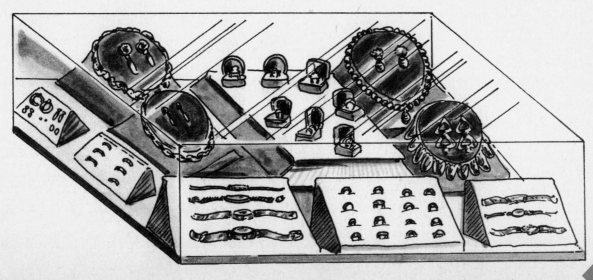

Directions Say each word. Write the number of vowels you see and the number of vowel sounds you hear.

		Vowels Seen	Vowel Sounds Heard			Vowels Seen	Vowel Sounds Heard
1.	remainder	____	____	24.	restaurant	____	____
2.	proceed	____	____	25.	lawbreaker	____	____
3.	mountain	____	____	26.	conveyance	____	____
4.	loafer	____	____	27.	passageway	____	____
5.	woeful	____	____	28.	loaded	____	____
6.	abstain	____	____	29.	lawnmower	____	____
7.	retreat	____	____	30.	greedily	____	____
8.	vein	____	____	31.	receivable	____	____
9.	daybreak	____	____	32.	autograph	____	____
10.	laundry	____	____	33.	maroon	____	____
11.	sprawl	____	____	34.	waterproof	____	____
12.	occupied	____	____	35.	bountiful	____	____
13.	toadstool	____	____	36.	power	____	____
14.	countless	____	____	37.	misunderstood	____	____
15.	likelihood	____	____	38.	woodpecker	____	____
16.	fried	____	____	39.	flaunt	____	____
17.	loosen	____	____	40.	circuit	____	____
18.	tablespoon	____	____	41.	wheelbarrow	____	____
19.	relieved	____	____	42.	guitar	____	____
20.	yield	____	____	43.	suitable	____	____
21.	applied	____	____	44.	billow	____	____
22.	encourage	____	____	45.	moisture	____	____
23.	announcer	____	____	46.	acquaintance	____	____

LESSON 28: Syllables

Name _____

Accidental Discoveries

Do you know the story of h_____
1

Christopher Columbus came to discover America by "mistake"? Supposedly, Columbus was so sure that the world was

r_____nd, not flat, that he thought he
2

could reach the Far East by sailing westward.

As we know, Columbus's v_____age led
3

him to islands in the Caribbean, not to the East Indies near Asia. But it seems to have taken some time before Columbus believed

that he and his cr_____ had touched
4

gr_____nd in a "n_____ world"
5   6

and not on an island off the coast of Japan or China.

Columbus was not the only European explorer whose discoveries came about by accident. Explorers like John Cabot first came to America in search of a short

r_____te to all_____ ships from
7   8

Britain to reach China and India. Others made their journeys with more unusual goals in mind. The Spanish explorer, Juan Ponce de León, for example, was searching for the

"f_____ntain of youth" when he came
9

upon an unsp_____led coast north of
10

Puerto Rico. He explored that coast in 1513, thinking that he had discovered a large island. He named it Florida which in

Spanish means "full of fl_____ers."
11

Francisco Coronado was another

explorer who was disapp_____nted in
12

what he f_____nd in the new world.
13

Coronado came to the American

S_____thwest in 1540. He was looking
14

for the Seven Cities of Cibola, a group of cities where riches were supposed to be so plentiful that the streets were paved with gold. For several years, Coronado's

l_____al band searched the
15

m_____ntains and deserts
16

with_____t success. Coronado never
17

did find Cibola's gold and j_____els.
18

What his army did find was the Grand Canyon, one of the most beautiful wonders of the world.

57

England's George Vancouver

George Vancover was born in Norfolk, England, in 1758. The British government sent a naval force, led by Vancouver, to the area. At age 13, Vancouver sailed with Captain Cook on that famous explorer's last two voyages.

Later, Vancouver joined the navy. His ship set sail in April of 1791. In 1793, Vancouver explored part of the American West Coast. He sailed by the Cape of Good Hope in Africa, Australia, and New Zealand, making maps of these areas as he traveled. Vancouver dealt with the situation of Nootka Sound promptly.

Vancouver is remembered as a British explorer who made some of the first maps of the South Pacific. He also surveyed the Pacific Coast of North America. Vancouver sailed in all kinds of weather. The charts Vancouver made of these areas were among the first maps Europeans had of the South Pacific. The maps proved extremely valuable to sailors in later years.

1. George Vancouver was born in Norfolk, Virginia. _____

2. Vancouver was an American explorer. _____

3. Vancouver's maps proved valuable to the sailors who came after him. _____

4. When he was only a teenager, Vancouver sailed with Captain Cook. _____

5. In 1793, Vancouver joined the navy. _____

6. Vancouver created some of the first maps of the Atlantic Ocean. _____

7. Vancouver made maps as he traveled past the Cape of Good Hope. _____

8. Vancouver surveyed the Pacific Coast of South America. _____

Name _____

Directions Circle the answer that best completes each sentence and write it on the line.

Hint Many words have special parts, or units of meaning, that help the reader to understand what the word means.

1. A base word is a <u>word</u> to which a prefix or suffix may be added to change its meaning.
Kind is the base word of **unkindly.**

   The base word of **unlawful** is _____.

   un   law   ful

2. The base word of **uncover** is _____.

   uncover   un   cover

3. The base word of **replaced** is _____.

   re   placed   place

4. A root is a <u>word part</u> to which a prefix or suffix may be added to change its meaning.
The root of **reduce** is **duce.**

   The root of **induction** is _____.

   duct   in   ion

5. The root for **propeller** is _____.

   propel   pel   er

6. A root or base word has _____.

   one word part   a prefix and a suffix   more than one word part

7. A prefix is a <u>word part</u> added in front of a root or a base word. **Un** is the prefix of **unhappy.**

   The prefix of **retied** is _____.

   ed   re   tie

8. The prefix of **subjection** is _____.

   ject   jection   sub

9. The prefix _____ the meaning of a root or base word.

   changes   doesn't   stops

10. A suffix is a <u>word part</u> added to the end of a root or base word. The suffix of **worker** is **er.**

    The suffix of **action** is _____.

    act   ion   a

11. The suffix of **contentment** is _____.

    ment   tent   content

59

	Base Word	Prefix	Suffix
1. unbeatable			
2. overflowing			
3. disagreement			
4. unsuccessful			
5. recounted			
6. semiannually			
7. unwholesome			

Directions List the root, prefix, and suffix of each word.

	Root	Prefix	Suffix
1. inspecting			
2. exportation			
3. projector			
4. distracted			
5. reduction			
6. injected			
7. disposal			

LESSON 30: Units of meanings in words

Name _____

	EXAMPLES		
Rule Un, dis, ir, im, and in are prefixes that usually mean *not*.	**Prefix**	**Word**	**Definition**
	un	**un**happy	not happy
	dis	**dis**approve	not approve
	ir	**ir**regular	not regular
	in	**in**expensive	not expensive
	im	**im**practical	not practical

Directions   Underline the word in each sentence that has a prefix meaning **not.** Then circle the prefix in that word.

1. One night Jo acted irresponsibly.
2. It was impossible for her to sleep.
3. Her bed was very uncomfortable.
4. Everything seemed disorganized.
5. Jo discovered her sister's diary.
6. She found the key and unlocked it.
7. Reading the book was irresistible.
8. Jo never thought it might be improper.
9. Jo's sister, Jan, disapproved of Jo's actions.
10. Jo was unable to understand why.
11. She felt that Jan was being unfair.
12. She believed Jan was irrational.

Directions   In each sentence below, there is a word which is missing the prefix **un, dis, ir,** or **in.** Write the prefix in the space provided.

1. Mary _____appears each evening after dinner.

2. She is _____happy if her privacy is interrupted.

3. Mary writes about things _____known to anyone but herself.

4. Her day seems _____complete without this special time.

5. Mary says her diary is _____replaceable.

6. She feels that it would be _____honest for others to read it.

61

Directions Use a prefix from the box to complete each base word. Write the correct word on the line.

un	dis	ir	in

1. Tony's baseball team has won every game and seems to be

   _____ this year.
   (beatable)

2. There has been _____ improvement since last season.
   (credible)

3. Last year there were many _____ .
   (advantages)

4. Practice was held at a time that was _____ for the players.
   (convenient)

5. Coach Lawson was very busy and his directions were _____ .
   (clear)

6. Because of their poor record, the players were _____ at
   (attentive)

   practice.

7. They were _____ and inconsiderate.
   (responsible)

8. No one is _____ with the way this
   (happy)

   year's season is progressing.

9. Coach Lawson won't look for any new players next season
   because he thinks they are all

   _____ !
   (replaceable)

LESSON 31: Prefixes UN-, DIS-, IR-, IN-

Name _____

Rule In and en are prefixes that can mean *cause to be* or *make*.

EXAMPLES		
Prefix	**Word**	**Definition**
in	**in**dent	to begin a line in from the margin
en	**en**tangle	to cause something to be tangled

Directions Fill in the circle under the word that completes each sentence.

1. Our class just finished a book _____ Treasures of the Kings.
   ○ entangled   ○ entitled   ○ enlarged

2. At first, some students seemed _____ to this kind of book.
   ○ inactive   ○ inflated   ○ indifferent

3. However, we were all _____ from the beginning to the end.
   ○ encrusted   ○ encaged   ○ engrossed

4. The book contained such vivid descriptions that we could almost see the words _____ on the treasures.
   ○ inhaled   ○ inhabited   ○ inscribed

5. The book _____ our knowledge of life in ancient Egypt.
   ○ inset   ○ increased   ○ indebted

6. It _____ in our minds the splendor of this period in history.
   ○ intoned   ○ ingrained   ○ indented

7. We were _____ to learn more about Ancient Egypt.
   ○ inspired   ○ inserted   ○ inspected

8. Reading the book has _____ our continued interest in ancient civilizations.
   ○ ensnarled   ○ enrobed   ○ ensured

9. We continue to read other books to _____ upon what we learned from Treasures of the Kings.
   ○ enlarge   ○ ennoble   ○ engorge

10. We all agreed that reading these books has _____ our lives.
    ○ enriched   ○ entangled   ○ entitled

63

____	**1.** entangled	**a.**	put in a cage
____	**2.** inhale	**b.**	breathe in
____	**3.** enchain	**c.**	live in or on
____	**4.** enrobe	**d.**	write on stone or paper
____	**5.** inhabit	**e.**	fasten something in place with a chain
____	**6.** inscribe	**f.**	get twisted and caught in
____	**7.** encage	**g.**	add to or grow
____	**8.** increase	**h.**	dress in a long, loose garment

Directions Look closely at the pictures and read their names. Then use the names to answer the questions.

king

cat

lion

bike

tire

_____ **1.** Which one is *inflated?*

_____ **2.** Which one is *encaged?*

_____ **3.** Which one is *enrobed?*

_____ **4.** Which one is *enchained?*

_____ **5.** Which one is *entangled?*

LESSON 32: Prefixes IN-, EN-

Name _____

<table>
<tr><td rowspan="3">Rule Mis and mal are prefixes that usually mean bad or badly.</td><td colspan="3">EXAMPLES</td></tr>
<tr><td>Prefix</td><td>Word</td><td>Definition</td></tr>
<tr><td>mis
mal</td><td>misbehave
maltreat</td><td>behave badly
treat badly</td></tr>
</table>

Directions Circle each word below in which **mis** or **mal** is used as a prefix.

1. mismatch
2. mallet
3. mister
4. maladjusted
5. mall
6. mislead
7. misuse
8. malformed
9. mistreated
10. misty
11. mistrusts
12. malnutrition
13. missile
14. misfortune
15. mistake
16. miscalculated

Directions Use one of the words you circled to complete each sentence.

1. Samson, the wildcat, had the _____ of being captured.

2. He _____ his own strength, and thought he was invincible.

3. Samson was _____, however, and could not move quickly.

4. He made the _____ of being overconfident.

5. After his capture, the hunters noticed that Samson had a _____ front paw.

6. They took him to the zoo, where he would not be _____.

7. Samson no longer suffers from _____.

8. As a matter of fact, Samson no longer _____ anyone.

65

1. **misfortune**   We had bad luck on our camping trip.

   _____

   _____

2. **misled**   Our guide was inexperienced, and we were led astray.

   _____

   _____

3. **misread**   She incorrectly read the map, and we took a wrong turn.

   _____

   _____

4. **miscalculated**   Then she incorrectly judged the distance back to our starting point.

   _____

   _____

5. **misbehaved**   Some members of our group acted badly and had to be reprimanded.

   _____

   _____

6. **maladjusted**   Others were badly adjusted to life outdoors.

   _____

   _____

7. **malnutrition**   Fortunately we were found before we began to suffer from lack of food.

   _____

   _____

LESSON 33: Prefixes MIS-, MAL-

Name _____

Directions Read the title and story below. Circle each word that begins with a prefix. Look for **un, dis, ir, im, in, en, mis,** and **mal.** You should circle 25 words in all.

The Impossible Child

Helen Keller is a model of great courage. She had two major disabilities. She was blind and also deaf. Because she was unable to see and hear, she also became mute—not able to talk. Cut off entirely from the world, Helen was a maladjusted child. She misbehaved often, causing discord in her home. She acted irresponsibly but her parents felt sorry for her. They thought she was incapable of improving her behavior.

Helen's parents became discouraged with their inability to help their unruly daughter. When she was seven, they sought help for her. Helen was entrusted to the insightful care of Anne Sullivan. Anne realized that Helen was not a stupid child. She did not pity her. She did not indulge her irresponsibility as Helen's parents had done.

When she began enforcing rules, Anne had to endure Helen's rebellious actions. Patiently, Anne tried to talk with Helen through the sense of touch, spelling out words in the little girl's hand. Then came an unforgettable day! Helen realized that Anne was spelling the word *water* in her hand. From then on, Helen's progress was unbelievably rapid.

Far from being a misfit in society, Helen became famous for her wisdom and courage. She lived a full, enriching life. She has inspired countless disabled people to overcome their handicaps and to live life to the fullest.

Directions Read each sentence. If the information is correct, write **yes.** If it is incorrect, write **no.**

1. Helen could see and hear, but not talk. _____

2. As a young child, Helen often behaved badly. _____

3. Helen's parents often punished her for her unruly behavior. _____

4. By the time Helen was seven, her parents were satisfied with the way she acted. _____

5. Anne Sullivan was often impatient with Helen. _____

6. Helen learned to lead a good, full life. _____

Directions Two sentences can often be combined into one sentence for smoother writing. Combine each sentence pair below. Use the word in parentheses ( ) that you see below each pair as your connecting word. Remember to put a comma before the connecting word.

1. Young Helen Keller was an unruly child. She became an inspiring adult.
   (but)

   Young Helen Keller was an unruly child, but she became an inspiring adult.

   _____

2. Helen Keller refused to feel disadvantaged. She did not let her handicaps keep her down.
   (and)

   _____

   _____

3. She even went to college. She graduated with honors.
   (and)

   _____

   _____

4. Helen was born with sight and hearing. An incurable disease destroyed these abilities when she was two.
   (but)

   _____

   _____

5. Helen wrote several books about her life. She wanted to encourage others who had disabilities.
   (because)

   _____

   _____

6. Helen needed help. Anne Sullivan came to stay in the Keller household.
   (so)

   _____

   _____

LESSON 34: Review and write

Name _____

Rules Pre and **pro** are prefixes that usually mean *before*. **Pro** can also mean *forward*.

EXAMPLES

Prefix	Word	Definition
pre	**pre**cook	to cook before
pro	**pro**ceed	to move ahead; to go forward

Directions Read each definition below. Choose a word from the box that fits it and write the word on the line beside its definition.

produce	predict	promotion
prejudge	prospective	preconceived

1. _____ being put forward in rank

2. _____ to form an opinion beforehand

3. _____ decided beforehand

4. _____ to bring forth

5. _____ to tell what one thinks will happen

6. _____ expected or likely

Directions Use a word from the box above to complete each sentence.

1. Dan's mother received an important _____ at work.

2. She interviews _____ employees for the company.

3. It is difficult to _____ which person will do the best job.

4. Mrs. Gale does not _____ those she interviews.

5. She tries not to have _____ ideas about people.

LESSON 35: Prefixes PRE-, PRO-

Circle each word below in which **pre** or **pro** is used as a prefix.

1. prepaid
2. prohibited
3. prepared
4. prolong
5. pretty
6. problem
7. precocious
8. preoccupy
9. prospective
10. premature
11. protested
12. prowl
13. proclaim
14. procrastinate
15. precious
16. proposed

Directions Write a word you circled to complete each sentence. Use each word only once.

1. Dad _____ a wonderful idea.

2. He suggested that we _____ our vacation.

3. No one _____ when Dad brought up the idea.

4. Since we had _____, we felt we could afford it.

5. Our plan was _____, however.

6. The hotel was full so we were _____ from staying.

7. We were disappointed as we _____ to leave.

8. We knew it would not help to _____, however.

LESSON 35: Prefixes PRE-, PRO-

Name _____

Rules Re is a prefix that means *again* or *back*. Ex is a prefix that means *out of* or *from*.

EXAMPLES

Prefix	Word	Definition
re	**re**call	call to mind again
	return	turn back
ex	**ex**port	to send goods from a country
	extend	to stretch out

Directions Read the story below. Then use the context to write definitions for the underlined words.

An Unexpected Delay

Carol was very excited about her pen pal's visit. She expected Maria to arrive shortly before noon on Saturday. On the way to the airport, the traffic had to be rerouted. The radio announcer reassured listeners that the detour would not be too lengthy. By the time Carol arrived at the airport she was exhausted. Maria was waiting and was relieved to see her. After Carol explained what had happened, the girls were able to relax.

1. **Excited** means _____ .

2. **Expected** means _____ .

3. **Rerouted** means _____ .

4. **Reassured** means _____ .

5. **Exhausted** means the same as _____ .

6. **Relieved** means _____ .

7. **Explained** means the same as _____ .

8. **Relax** means _____ .

LESSON 36: Prefixes RE-, EX-

1. reassure
2. reading
3. rewash
4. ready
5. retrace
6. exciting
7. explain
8. reprint
9. relocate
10. recreate
11. remedy
12. expand
13. reason
14. rearrange
15. regal
16. replaced
17. resident
18. expressed
19. refused
20. remembered

Directions Write a word you circled to complete each sentence.

1. Amanda was thrilled when she learned that her family had to

_____ to a new state.

2. She anticipated many _____ adventures.

3. Amanda _____ the last time she had moved.

4. She was eager to make new friends, but knew that her other friends could not be

_____ .

5. Amanda's sister _____ to be happy.

6. She _____ concern and anger.

7. Amanda tried to _____ why she was so delighted.

8. She tried to _____ her sister that things would work out.

Name _____

EXAMPLES

Prefix	Word	Definition
fore	**fore**head	front of the head
post	**post**script	message written after a letter

Directions Write the letter of each word on the line beside its definition.

_____ 1. A time before noon

_____ 2. Put off until later

_____ 3. An ability to see ahead and know about something before it happens

_____ 4. A message added after the signature of a letter

_____ 5. To predict what is coming before it happens

_____ 6. Generations after us; people of the future

a. postscript
b. foresight
c. posterity
d. postpone
e. forenoon
f. forecast

Directions Write a word from the list above to complete each sentence.

1. Our class wrote letters for _____.

2. We planned to seal them in a time capsule in the _____ on Friday.

3. We wanted to describe our present lives and to _____ the future.

4. Mark didn't use _____ in planning his time wisely.

5. He was adding a _____ as the clock struck twelve.

6. We were disappointed when our teacher said we had to _____ the project until Monday.

73

Directions Answer each question with a word from the box. Then use the words to complete the crossword puzzle.

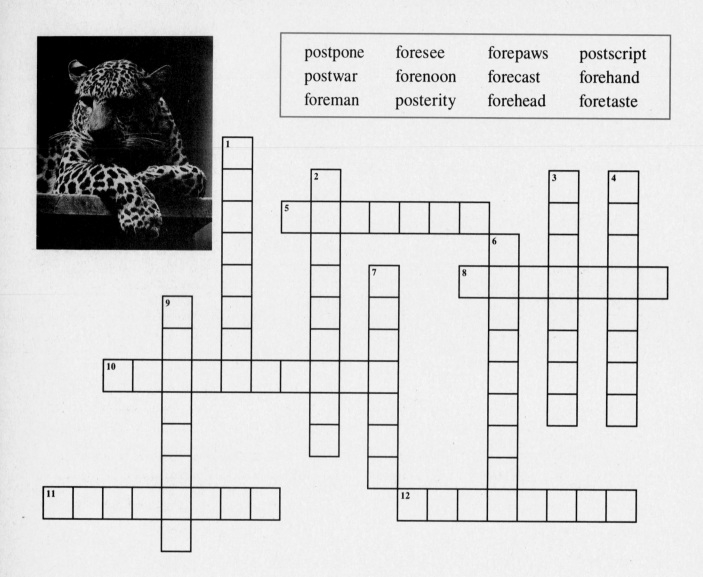

postpone	foresee	forepaws	postscript
postwar	forenoon	forecast	forehand
foreman	posterity	forehead	foretaste

Across

5. What is the person in charge of a work crew called?
8. What does a prophet supposedly do with the future?
10. What do the letters *P.S.* at the end of a letter stand for?
11. What period of the day is 11 o'clock in the morning?
12. What is the name of a type of stroke used in tennis?

Down

1. What are the front feet of an animal called?
2. Who are the generations that live *after* us?
3. What does a weatherperson do?
4. What do hair bangs cover?
6. What is a sample of what is to come?
7. What do you call the period of time after war?
9. Which word means "put off an event until a later date"?

LESSON 37: Prefixes FORE-, POST-

Name _____

Directions Read the story. Circle each word that begins with one of these prefixes: **fore, ex, re, pre, pro.** You will circle 30 words.

A Real American Princess

Matoaka was a real American princess. More often referred to as Pocahontas, Matoaka grew up in the wild expanse of what is now Virginia. It is not known exactly when she was born, because the Indians did not record births or deaths. Experts say she was born around the year 1595.

Her father, Powhatan, was one of the foremost chiefs in the region. He loved his daughter. He protected and provided for her. As a little girl, Pocahontas did the chores expected of her. She excelled in sewing and in making beads. Sometimes she had to restring the beads. Her mother provided excellent training.

One day when Pocahontas was exploring near the coast with some friends, she saw a huge ship. The men getting off this strange ship did not resemble Indians. Their faces were almost white. No one could have foreseen then that this group would establish the colony of Jamestown.

Chief Powhatan and his tribe expressed fear of these "palefaces." They soon captured the leader, Captain John Smith, and prepared to kill him. Pocahontas, then about 12 years old, protested when she saw the captain tied hand and foot. Her cries resounded throughout the village. She pleaded with her father to reconsider, but he pretended not to hear her. Pocahontas saw

that she could not forestall Smith's death with tears or pleas. So just as they were about to kill Captain Smith, Pocahontas, with no forewarning, ran out and stood by him. If they killed him, they would have to kill her, too. Pocahontas exhibited great courage and preserved the life of John Smith. She and Captain Smith remained friends as long as they lived.

Some years later, Pocahontas fell in love with a young Englishman named John Rolfe. When her father discovered that she wanted to marry an Englishman, he was angry. But Powhatan could not prevent the wedding, and Pocahontas was married to John Rolfe. She and her husband went to England a few years later, so Pocahontas could be presented to King James and Queen Anne. When she met them, they liked her and renamed her Lady Rebecca.

LESSON 38: Review and write

1. The real name of Pocahontas was Matoaka. _____

2. The Indians always wrote down the dates of births and deaths among their tribe. _____

3. Powhatan was a very important chief. _____

4. The men who came on the strange ship looked exactly like Indians. _____

5. Pocahontas was not very brave. _____

6. Powhatan saved John Smith because his daughter protested so loudly. _____

7. Pocahontas's mother gave her very good training. _____

8. Powhatan did not want his daughter to marry an Englishman. _____

9. Powhatan was able to stop the wedding from taking place. _____

10. In England, Pocahontas was given the name of Lady Rebecca. _____

Directions Two sentences can often be combined into one sentence for smoother writing. Combine each sentence pair below by using the word in parentheses ( ) as your connecting word. Remember to put a comma before the connecting word.

1. John Rolfe proposed marriage to Pocahontas. Pocahontas accepted. (and)

   _____

   _____

2. Powhatan did not approve of his daughter's marriage. John Rolfe was an Englishman. (because)

   _____

   _____

3. Pocahontas married John Rolfe. She and Captain John Smith remained friends for life. (but)

   _____

   _____

LESSON 38: Review and write

Name _____

Rule When **over** is used as a prefix, it means *too* or *too much*. If an adjective begins with **over**, it usually means *too*. If a verb begins with **over**, the prefix usually means *too much*.

EXAMPLES

overlong	**over**exercise
overeager	**over**spend
overbold	**over**heat

Directions Choose a word from the box that completes each sentence and write it on the line. Use each word only once.

1. The gymnasium was _____ the night of the big game.

2. Some of the crowd _____ into the hallway.

3. The vendors had _____ their popcorn and hot dogs.

4. Some of the beverages were warm and _____ .

5. The fans didn't seem to mind if they _____ , though.

6. The players knew they could win but were not _____ .

7. They warmed up but were careful not to _____ .

8. They had trained long and hard, and hoped not to become _____ .

9. After the victory the sport announcers were _____ with their praise.

10. They gave their listeners an exciting _____ of the game.

overexercise
overtired
overcrowded
overconfident
overflowed
overpriced
overgenerous
overspent
overview
oversweet

77

LESSON 39: The prefix OVER-

1. Mr. Taylor was ____ when he opened his new restaurant.
    ○ overprotective   ○ overconfident   ○ overtalkative

2. It was located in an ____ area so he anticipated a great deal of business.
    ○ overambitious   ○ overpopulated   ○ overspent

3. On the day of the grand opening the restaurant was ____.
    ○ overcrowded   ○ overtired   ○ overeager

4. It was very warm and many of the customers became ____.
    ○ overpriced   ○ overheated   ○ overgenerous

5. The hostess was ____ and annoyed some of the patrons.
    ○ overtalkative   ○ overpriced   ○ overpopulated

6. The waitresses were ____ taking care of so many customers.
    ○ overthrown   ○ overworked   ○ overbalanced

7. Much of the food was ____ and unappetizing.
    ○ overspent   ○ overcooked   ○ overeager

8. The customers couldn't finish their orders because the portions were ____.
    ○ overstocked   ○ overgenerous   ○ overweight

9. People felt the meals were ____ and were disappointed with Mr. Taylor's new establishment.
    ○ overused   ○ overserious   ○ overpriced

10. Some customers stopped coming, so the restaurant was ____ with food.
    ○ overstepped   ○ overlooked   ○ overstocked

11. Mr. Taylor ____ and considered closing the restaurant.
    ○ overreacted   ○ overplayed   ○ overdressed

LESSON 39: The prefix OVER-

Name _____

EXAMPLES

Prefix	Word	Definition
co	**co**operate	to work with others
com	**com**bine	to join together
con	**con**spire	to plan secretly

Directions Write the word from the box on the line next to its meaning.

_____ **1.** to rival

_____ **2.** to be victorious

_____ **3.** competitors in a game

_____ **4.** leading actors appearing with one another in the same show

_____ **5.** to make complete or bring to perfection

> contestants
> complement
> Conquer
> compete
> costars

Directions Use the words from the box above to complete each sentence.

1. My favorite television show is called "Can You _____?"

2. Each week there are two _____ on the program.

3. The guests _____ for fabulous prizes.

4. Charlie Cash and Polly Prize are the _____ of the show.

5. They make a good team because their personalities _____ each other.

CAN YOU CONQUER?

LESSON 40: Prefixes CO-, COM-, CON-

cochairmen	consisted	committee
Consequently	competitive	convinced
consented	comfortably	cooperate
combination	conversation	

1. Brian is very _____.

2. He finds it difficult to _____ with others.

3. _____, he does not work well in groups.

4. Once Brian was asked to head a _____ at school.

5. The group _____ of eight of his classmates.

6. There was very little _____ at the quiet meetings.

7. Brian _____ his best friend to join the committee.

8. His friend _____ after much persuasion.

9. The two boys worked as _____ of the group.

10. They made a great _____!

11. The members then were able to work together _____.

LESSON 40: Prefixes CO-, COM-, CON-

Name _____

Rules Sub can mean *under, below,* or *not quite.* **Mid** can mean the *middle part.*

EXAMPLES

A **subway** train travels under the ground.
Midnight is the middle part of the night.

Directions Read each definition. Then add the prefix **mid** or **sub** to the beginning of the word to make a word that fits the definition.

1. a ship that goes under sea: _____ marine

2. halfway; in the middle: _____ way

3. put down or overcome by superior force; conquer: _____ due

4. a person below another in rank: _____ ordinate

5. air above the ground; in the middle of the air: _____ air

6. existing below the conscious; not fully recognized in the mind: _____ conscious

7. middle of the week; Wednesday: _____ week

8. middle of a stream: _____ stream

Directions Follow the directions to finish the picture in the box below.

1. Draw a **submarine** in **midocean.**
2. Draw a jogger who is **midway** over the bridge.
3. Draw a large fish in **midstream.**
4. Draw an airplane in **midair.**

81

1. **Which day occurs midweek?**

   Sunday   Friday   Wednesday

2. **Which animal would you look for in midstream?**

   robin   mouse   fish

3. **Which of these travels underwater?**

   ship   submarine   subway train

4. **When is midday?**

   noon   10 a.m.   2 p.m.

5. **Which one is in the midriff area?**

   leg   neck   waistline

6. **Which one is an underground railway?**

   subsoil   subset   subway

7. **When is midnight?**

   twelve o'clock at night   10 o'clock at night   6 o'clock at night

8. **Which word is an antonym of subtract?**

   divide   add   multiply

9. **What happens to a storm that subsides?**

   It dies down.   It causes damage.   It gets stronger.

LESSON 41: Prefixes SUB-, MID-

Name _____

EXAMPLES

A **bicycle** has two wheels.
A **tripod** has three legs.

Directions Choose the word from the box that describes each picture, and write it on the line.

bifocals	triangle	biplane	biceps
trio	binoculars	triplets	tripod

1.

_____

2.

_____

3.

_____

4.

_____

5.

_____

6.

_____

7.

_____

8.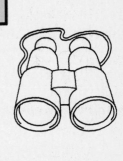

_____

Directions Use each word from the list in a sentence of your own.

1. bifocals _____

2. triangle _____

3. binoculars _____

4. tripod _____

83

binoculars	triplets	Bicentennial	tricycles
Tricentennial	bifocals	tricolored	

The U. S. Bicentennial

On July 4, 1976, the United States became 200 years old. It was the biggest and best birthday party Americans had ever seen—the Great

_____ .
1

For weeks before the big day, people splashed red, white, and blue paint all over America. Some children painted each wheel

of their _____ with
2
one of the three patriotic colors. On the day itself, one set of

_____ paraded in
3
New York, each one dressed in one of the flag colors. One man even sported a

_____ beard! The
4
original Declaration of Independence was displayed in Washington, D.C. The lines of people waiting to see it were so long that some people used

_____ to view the
5
document from a distance. Those who got close did not need to wear

_____ to read the
6
bold signature of John Hancock!

In 2076, America will celebrate its

_____ . How old will
7
you be?

Directions Circle each word in which **bi** or **tri** is used as a prefix.

bimonthly	billboard	tripod	tribute
trickle	bitter	binoculars	tricycle
bicycle	biscuit	bias	biceps
trilogy	bilingual	triceps	trivia

LESSON 42: Prefixes BI-, TRI-

Name _____

Directions Read the story. Circle each word that begins with one of these prefixes: **over, bi, tri, sub, mid, con, co, com.** You will circle 17 words.

Willie Mays

Willie Mays was a baseball superstar. He contracted to play with the New York Giants in 1950, when he was only nineteen years old. This made Willie one of the first black people to be admitted to major league baseball. The first person to make the game of baseball biracial had been Jackie Robinson, three years earlier. Never one to be overconfident, Willie felt at first that he could not compete well enough to be in a major league. At midseason of his first year, his batting record was poor. The manager helped Willie conquer his fears by telling him he was overanxious and should not worry so much. The manager said that he would not send such a fine player as Willie back to the minors.

It may have been the most commendable decision ever made by the manager. Willie went on to subject opposing teams to defeat after defeat. He had an outstanding combination of baseball talents.

His coequal, Joe DiMaggio, made this comment about Mays: "This man does it all. He hits, he fields, he runs, he studies, he hardly ever makes mistakes."

Mays hit plenty of singles, doubles, and triples. But he is especially remembered for the long list of home runs he compiled—660 in all. In the 1954 World Series, Willie made one overhead catch in midair while on the run. It is considered one of the most outstanding plays in baseball history.

Directions Answer each question about the story by writing **yes** or **no.**

_____ **1.** Did Willie Mays sign a major league contract when he was 19 years old?

_____ **2.** Was Willie the first black man to play for the major leagues?

_____ **3.** At first, was Willie unsure of his own ability?

_____ **4.** Had Willie compiled a superb batting record by the middle of his first year in the major leagues?

_____ **5.** Did Willie have several baseball talents?

_____ **6.** Does the writer of this story seem to think that Willie was superior in baseball to Joe DiMaggio?

_____ **7.** Did Willie dive to capture a ground ball in his famous catch of 1954?

1. At one time, black people didn't play for the major leagues. Jackie Robinson broke the racial barrier. (but)

   _____

   _____

2. The Giants at first paid Willie $5,000. They later gave him a $100,000 contract. (but)

   _____

   _____

3. Willie's dad was a semipro baseball player. Will was "brought up" on the game. (so)

   _____

   _____

1. Willie Mays, the solid superstar, was five feet, eleven inches tall. He weighed one hundred eighty-five pounds.

   _____

   _____

2. Willie played for the Giants during most of his career. He was traded to the Mets in 1972.

   _____

   _____

   _____

3. Willie Mays made many sensational plays. He is best remembered for his numerous home runs.

   _____

   _____

   _____

LESSON 43: Review and write

Name _____

EXAMPLES

pos usually means *put* or *place* (**pos**ition)
pel or **pul** usually means *push* or *drive* (pro**pel**)

Directions Write the number of each word on the line beside its definition.

1. pulse   _____   driven or forced away from something unpleasant

2. compelled   _____   heartbeat felt as blood is pushed through the arteries

3. positive   _____   put out of a person's mind

4. deposit   _____   certain of one's position

5. dispel   _____   driven to do something

6. dispose   _____   set forth a position or opinion

7. propose   _____   put or place somewhere

8. repelled   _____   get rid of, put away from

Directions Read the sentences and underline the words that contain the roots **pos, pel,** or **pul.**

1. Mrs. Estes felt repelled whenever she saw a creepy, crawly object.
2. When she saw an ant or a spider her pulse would race.
3. Friends tried to dispel her fears.
4. Nevertheless, she was positive her odd reaction had a good side.
5. She felt compelled to keep her house bug free.
6. She disposed of garbage every day.
7. She deposited the garbage cans far from the house.
8. "I propose that my fear makes me an excellent housekeeper!" she said.

87

EXAMPLES

port means *carry* (**port**able)
ject means *throw* or *force* (e**ject**)

Directions Read the words below. Underline each word in which you see the root **port.** Circle each word in which you see the root **ject.**

1. portfolio
2. ejector
3. porter
4. important
5. reject
6. subject
7. reporter
8. portable
9. injection
10. transport
11. projector
12. adjectives

Directions Write the word from the list above that correctly completes the sentence.

1. Mr. Casey flew to Boston to give an _____ speech.

2. The _____ was "Advances in Space Travel."

3. He planned to _____ equipment so he could show a film.

4. As the _____ carried the bags into the hotel, Mr. Casey noticed that something was missing.

5. He had forgotten to bring the film _____.

6. "I hope my verbs and _____ are colorful enough to substitute for the film!" he said.

Name _____

Hint Knowing the meaning of a word root helps you figure out the meaning of a new word.

EXAMPLES

aud means *hear* (**aud**ience)
dict means *tell* or *say* (pre**dict**)

Directions Choose the word from the list at the right that correctly completes each sentence. Write the word on the line.

1. Kim was class _____ at her college graduation.

2. Her teachers _____ she would soon find a job.

3. Kim found a job typing and taking

   _____.

4. She worked for a producer of _____ displays.

5. When typing, she used a device called a

   _____.

6. Kim said that her boss mumbled a lot and had poor

   _____.

7. Sometimes his words were barely _____

8. When unsure of words, she found a _____ very helpful.

audiovisual
dictionary
valedictorian
dictaphone
predicted
audible
dictation
diction

Directions Circle the word that correctly completes each sentence, and write it on the line.

1. A ruler who has power over everybody in a country is a _____.
   predictor   dictator   indicter

2. A group of people gathered to hear and see something is an _____.
   audience   auditorium   audiometer

3. To say something that is opposite of what someone else has said is to

   _____.

   contravene   contraband   contradict

EXAMPLES
Root: **duct**, **duce** usually mean *lead* (con**duct**)
scribe, **script** usually mean *write* or *something written* (in**scribe**)
Prefix: **intro** usually means *in* or *into* (**intro**duce)
e usually means *from* or *away* (**e**ject)
re usually means *back* or *again* (**re**duce)

Directions Read each word in the list. Underline the prefix and circle the root in each word.

1. describe
2. subscribe
3. conscript
4. education
5. reduce
6. deduce
7. conduct
8. subscriptions
9. introduce
10. educe
11. produce
12. deduct

Directions Use a word from the box above to complete each sentence. The roots and prefixes will help you find the correct word.

1. Rick decided to make money by selling magazine _____.

2. He would knock on doors, _____ himself, and ask for orders.

3. Then he would _____ the various magazines on his list.

4. To promote sales, he offered to _____ the cost of the first issue from the total bill.

5. He found that this was a good way to _____ his profits even though it increased his sales.

6. The experience added greatly to his math _____.

LESSON 45: Roots DUCT, DUCE, SCRIBE, SCRIPT

Name _____

EXAMPLES

spec, spect usually mean *see*, *look*, or *examine*
mit, miss usually mean *send* or *let go*

Directions Read the sentences and underline the words that contain the roots **spec, spect, mit,** or **miss.**

1. Mr. Clark, an attorney, inspected the evidence at the scene of the crime.
2. At first, he dismissed all the items as being unimportant.
3. He permitted his assistant, Miss Grant, to examine the evidence.
4. He respected her opinion and was eager to hear it.
5. Miss Grant speculated about the items and concluded that one of them was important!
6. Mr. Clark thought about it and admitted that he had been wrong.
7. He decided to submit the item as evidence at the trial.
8. As a result, the suspect was convicted.

Directions Write the number of each word beside its meaning

1. permit   _____ to look at someone or something with mistrust
2. prospect   _____ a person who watches or looks at something
3. dismiss   _____ a future possibility one is looking for
4. suspect   _____ a period between acts in a play
5. respect   _____ to let or allow
6. spectator   _____ to send from one's mind
7. admit   _____ to look at a person with admiration
8. intermission _____ to let enter one's mind

LESSON 46: Roots SPEC, SPECT, MIT, MISS

Rule The roots **fac, fect, fic,** and **feit** can mean *do, make,* or *cause.*

EXAMPLES
EXAMPLES

factory   per**fect**   **fic**tion   for**feit**

Directions Read the words in the box. Circle the root **fac, fect, fic,** or **feit** in each word.

defective	facsimile	fictitious
factory	counterfeit	benefactor
fiction	effect	perfect

Directions Use the words in the list to work the crossword puzzle below.

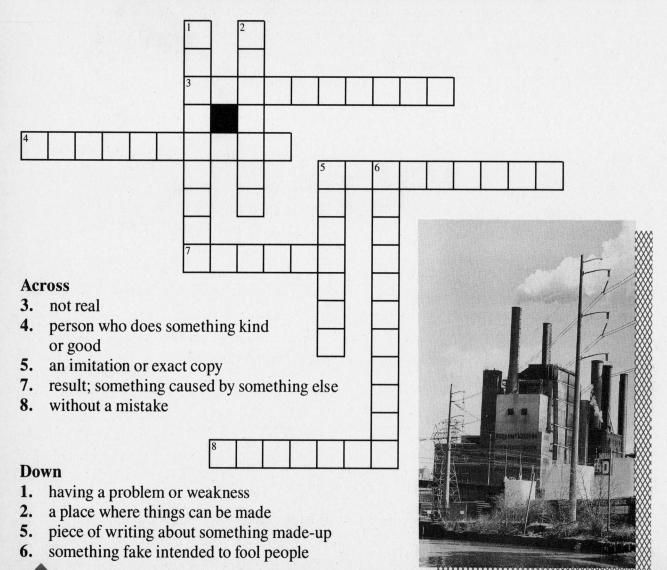

Across
3. not real
4. person who does something kind or good
5. an imitation or exact copy
7. result; something caused by something else
8. without a mistake

Down
1. having a problem or weakness
2. a place where things can be made
5. piece of writing about something made-up
6. something fake intended to fool people

LESSON 46: Roots FAC, FECT, FIC, FEIT

Name _____

Directions The words in the box have roots that you studied in this unit. Read the words and then read the story. Choose the correct word from the box to complete each sentence, and write it on the line.

---

audibly	reporter	defective
position	projector	ejector
audience	contradict	received

The Big Surprise

Miss Carson was leaving her teaching

_____ to become a
　　　1

_____ for the *Suburban*
　　　2

Times. Her fifth-grade class wanted to surprise her. They wanted to do something different.

"Let's have a piñata party," suggested Carlos.

"I don't like to _____
　　　　　　　　　　　　　3

your suggestion, Carlos," said Lisa, "but we had one at Christmas."

"We could have a slide show," said Heidi.

Everyone liked Heidi's idea. They decided to invite the other fifth-grade class so they would have an

_____. Bill was sure
　　　4

his brother would let them use the slide

_____ he had just
　　　5

_____ for his birthday.
　　　6

When Bill tried to use it, the slides wouldn't drop down and pop up the way they were supposed to. There was something

wrong with the _____.
　　　　　　　　　　　　　　7

Fortunately, Bill quickly found the

_____ part and replaced it
　　　8

with a new one.

The party was a huge success. Miss Carson was so surprised when she saw the slide show that she gasped

_____.
　　　9

"Thank you," she said. "You are a wonderful class! I will always remember you!"

93

Directions   Read the following paragraph. Choose the sentence that tells the main idea of the paragraph. Then write it on the line below the paragraph.

Definition   The **main idea** sentence tells what a paragraph is about. It can be found anywhere in the paragraph. All the other sentences should give details about the main idea.

Last night I had to forfeit my chance to play basketball. I was a mere spectator. How dejected I felt! My foot had become infected, and my doctor would not permit me to play. It was hard to be submissive to the doctor's orders.

_____

Directions   Now reread the paragraph, and circle each word that has a root that you have learned about in this unit. Write the words on the lines below. Then put a box around each root.

_____   _____

_____   _____

_____   _____

Name _____

EXAMPLES

cupcake = cup + cake
doghouse = dog + house
snowstorm = snow + storm

Directions Read each sentence and underline each compound word. Be sure the words you underline are made up of two words that can stand on their own.

1. Captain Orr spun the dials on the dashboard of the spaceship.
2. He pointed the ship's nose toward the sunrise.
3. The countdown and the blastoff went smoothly.
4. The launch, cancelled twice by bad weather, had been overdue.
5. Now came the payoff for the long training of the spacemen.
6. Word of the successful launch was being broadcast countrywide.
7. Dugan watched Captain Orr chew calmly on a toothpick.
8. It was his first flight, and he felt like a boy on his birthday.
9. Someday he would tell his grandchildren of this great adventure.

Directions Find the correct compound word from those you underlined above to match each definition below. Write the word on the line.

1. the instrument panel on a vehicle

   _____

2. a vehicle used for travel in outer space

   _____

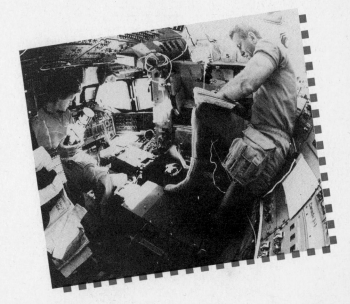

3. beginning of day

   _____

4. the very first stage of a space trip

   _____

5. a reward for hard work

   _____

95

1.			2.		3.		
rain	bread	cup	cake	pan		fish
grape	fly	cat	coat	pea		shirt
earth	fruit	over	meal	sweat		links
blue	bird	neck	socks	star		cakes
corn	worm	knee	fish	cuff		nut
horse	coat	oat	tie	lady		bug

Kinds of food

1. _____
2. _____
3. _____
4. _____
5. _____
6. _____

Things to wear

1. _____
2. _____
3. _____
4. _____
5. _____
6. _____

Kinds of animals

1. _____
2. _____
3. _____
4. _____
5. _____
6. _____

LESSON 48: Compound words

Name _____

Definition This mark (') is called an **apostrophe**. An 's can be added to a word to show ownership or possession.

EXAMPLES

Ella has a book. This is Ella's book.

The 's after Ella shows that Ella owns or has a book.

Directions Read each sentence. Then fill in the circle beside the word that correctly completes the sentence.

1. Tom threw back the ____ on his bed.

   ○ covers
   ○ cover's

2. His ____ growling confirmed his hunger.

   ○ stomach
   ○ stomach's

3. The ____ creaked as he crept down for a late-night snack.

   ○ stairs
   ○ stair's

4. He heard his ____ voice in the living room.

   ○ mothers
   ○ mother's

5. Sunday was the ____ tenth birthday.

   ○ boys
   ○ boy's

6. His ____ were planning a surprise party.

   ○ parents
   ○ parent's

7. On Sunday, he heeded his ____ call to come downstairs.

   ○ sisters
   ○ sister's

8. Twenty ____ yelled "Happy birthday!"

   ○ voices
   ○ voice's

9. A ____ wheels peeked through a huge package.

   ○ bikes
   ○ bike's

10. ____ surprise was real, but it had nothing to do with the party.

   ○ Toms
   ○ Tom's

EXAMPLES

Sally**'s** coat

the boys**'** coats

the children**'s** coats

Directions Read each sentence below. Write the correct possessive form of the word you see below the line. Look back at the rules if you need to.

1. _____ greatest wish was to explore caves.
   Maria

2. Many caves dot her _____ hills.
   community

3. She tried to get her _____ permission.
   parents

4. "It isn't a safe _____ hobby," her mother said.
   children

5. Her dad belongs to a _____ club for cave explorers.
   men

6. She finally got her _____ promise to take her along.
   father

7. On the _____ first visit they heard a strange noise.
   pair

8. It was the sound of hundreds of _____ wings.
   bats

9. Maria hasn't asked to explore a _____ mouth since.
   cave

Name _____

Definition A **contraction** is a short way of writing two words. The two words are written together with one or more letters left out. An apostrophe stands for the missing letters.

EXAMPLES

it is = it's (The letter **i** has been left out.)
I will = I'll (The letters **wi** have been left out.)
we are = we're (The letter **a** has been left out.)

Directions On the first line, write the contraction from the box that stands for each pair of words. Then, on the second line, write the letter or letters that have been left out.

| wouldn't | you're | they'll | didn't |
| we're | I'm | it's | I've |

1. we are _____we're_____ ___a___

2. did not _____ _____

3. I am _____ _____

4. would not _____ _____

5. they will _____ _____

6. you are _____ _____

7. it is _____ _____

8. I have _____ _____

| can't | she'll | you've | that's |
| let's | isn't | he's |

1. she will _____ _____

2. you have _____ _____

3. is not _____ _____

4. let us _____ _____

5. he is _____ _____

6. can not _____ _____

7. that is _____ _____

99

The Kooky Clock

Sara climbed out of bed grumbling to herself. "I don't believe it! The one day I have to be up early, my alarm clock doesn't go off. If Henry had anything to do with this, I'll have something to say to him!"

She stumbled into her clothes, still half asleep. Her shoes didn't fit, and she realized she hadn't put them on the right feet. "Let's get this together," she muttered. "I'm not going to miss the last day of the spelling contest. Nancy's going to be at school early. I know she'll be there before anybody else so she can get some extra study time."

Finally Sara was ready. She raced down the stairs, not even stopping to grab her book. As she ran outside she bumped into her brother Henry on the porch.

"What kept you?" he asked.

"My alarm clock didn't go off."

"I hope I wasn't at fault. I set it last night so it would go off early," Henry explained. "At least that's what I thought I did."

"Well, you've got a lot to learn about clocks," said Sara. "Come on, or we'll both be late!"

1. _____

2. _____

3. _____

4. _____

5. _____

6. _____

7. _____

8. _____

9. _____

10. _____

11. _____

12. _____

13. _____

14. _____

Name _____

Rule A word has as many syllables as it has vowel sounds. A prefix is a syllable in itself if it contains a vowel sound. Divide the word between the prefix and the base word. Remember that some prefixes have more than one syllable.

1. dispose _____ _____

2. subject _____ _____

3. predict _____ _____

4. audible _____ _____

5. introduce _____ _____

6. reduce _____ _____

7. permit _____ _____

8. spectator _____ _____

9. defect _____ _____

10. posture _____ _____

11. subdivide _____ _____

12. biennial _____ _____

13. transport _____ _____

14. dictation _____ _____

15. subscribe _____ _____

16. mission _____ _____

17. counterfeit _____ _____

18. perfect _____ _____

19. deceive _____ _____

20. expect _____ _____

21. conduct _____ _____

22. reporter _____ _____

23. postscript _____ _____

24. submerge _____ _____

Directions Read each sentence, find the missing word, and write it on the line.

1. Mom said I could _____ to the magazine for the summer.

subscribe
subject

2. The news _____ interviewed the girl who saved the drowning child.

reporter
spectator

Rules Divide a compound word between the two words that make up the compound word. Then, divide the smaller words into syllables.

EXAMPLES

peanut   pea/nut

underground   under/ground   un/der/ground

Directions Divide each compound word into two words, using vertical lines. If necessary, divide the smaller words into syllables.

1. mailbox _____

2. strawberry _____

3. everyone _____

4. skyscraper _____

5. seashore _____

6. footprints _____

7. buttonhole _____

8. overcoat _____

9. clothespin _____

10. classmate _____

11. anthill _____

12. workbook _____

13. wristwatch _____

14. sailboat _____

Directions Write the word from above that completes each sentence.

1. This year the class outing was held at the _____.

2. One _____ had never seen the ocean before.

3. Sarah saw a sand dune and thought it was a giant _____.

4. Carl enjoyed watching a _____ drift along the horizon.

5. Louis searched for _____ in the sand.

6. At the end of the day, _____ went home tired but happy.

Name _____

Directions Read the contractions, possessives, and compound words in the box. Then write the correct words to complete the sentences.

He'll	ladybug's	there's	hummingbirds
she'd	spiderweb	Katie's	volleyball
butterfly	anteaters	earthworms	I'm

The people in my family are crazy about animals. _____ most
                                                        1
interested in animals that fly. Yesterday she said _____ seen two
                                                              2
_____ and a swallowtail _____ on her way to
        3   4
_____ practice. Then _____ Ricky, my brother.
        5   6
His favorite creatures are crawling things, like insects and _____ .
                                                                        7
_____ always stop for hours to observe a spider spinning a
        8
_____ . He likes the _____ spots. Now
        9   10
_____ more sensible! I especially like animals with long snouts, such as
        11
elephants and _____ .
                    12

Directions Read the following sentences. Decide which one states the main idea of the paragraph and write **MI** next to it. Figure out which two are supporting details and write **SD** next to each. Put an **X** next to the sentence that does not say anything about the paragraph.

1. _____ The writer's friend does not like animals at all.

2. _____ The writer likes animals with long snouts.

3. _____ The writer's brother watches spiders spin webs.

4. _____ The writer's family enjoys watching animals.

apostrophe	contraction	possessive
	syllables	compound

1. A _____ is a short way of writing two words.

2. An _____ stands for the letter or letters that are missing.

3. A _____ form shows that someone or something owns, has, or possesses something.

4. A _____ word is made up of two smaller words that can stand alone.

5. There are many rules for dividing words into parts.

   These word parts are called _____ .

_____   _____

_____   _____

_____

Directions Write two sentences about the apostrophe. Write about the different ways it is used. In your sentences try to use a contraction and a possessive. Also see if you can include a compound word.

_____

_____

_____

_____

_____

_____

_____

   LESSON 52: Review and write

Name _____

Rules The suffixes **er** and **or** can change a verb into a noun that means *someone who does something* or *a thing that can do something*. The suffix **ist** changes one kind of noun into another kind of noun that means *someone who does something*.

EXAMPLES

Verb	Noun
read	read**er**
collect	collect**or**

Noun	Noun
science	scient**ist**

Directions Add **er, or,** or **ist** to each word to make a noun. If a word ends with **e,** remember to drop the **e** before adding the suffix.

1. interpret _____
2. teach _____
3. real _____
4. train _____
5. counsel _____
6. archaeology _____
7. novel _____
8. bake _____
9. project _____
10. visit _____

Directions Write one of the words you made above to complete each sentence.

1. Nancy fixed up the guest room for a special _____.

2. Nancy's school _____ had assigned her an exchange student.

3. Nancy thought they would need an _____ to communicate.

4. Her guest speaks English as well as an English _____.

5. Her guest wants to be an _____ who studies old cities.

6. Nancy says she'd like to be a best-selling _____.

105

LESSON 53: Suffixes -ER, -OR, -IST

EXAMPLES

Word	Definition
sky**ward**	in the direction of the sky
loos**en**	to cause to be loose
gold**en**	made of gold
equal**ize**	to cause to be equal

Directions Underline the word in each sentence with the suffix **ward, en,** or **ize.** Then write a short definition of the word on the line.

1. Dan and Sue decided to modernize their old house.

   Modernize means _____.

2. They selected some pretty woolen carpeting for the floors.

   Woolen means _____.

3. They also decided to shorten the floor-length curtains.

   Shorten means _____.

4. Tired, they felt they were going backward and making no progress.

   Backward means _____.

5. They decided to go and buy some wooden bookshelves.

   Wooden means _____.

6. When they returned, they saw that a lovely room was beginning to materialize.

   Materialize means _____.

7. They were revitalized and ready to work again.

   Revitalize means _____.

LESSON 53: Suffixes -WARD, -EN, -IZE

Name _____

Rule The suffixes **er** and **est** are added to adjectives to make them show comparison.

EXAMPLES

Today is **hot**.
Today is **hotter** than yesterday. (Two days are compared.)
Today is the **hottest** day of the year. (More than two days are compared.)

Directions Read each sentence and the two words below the line. Choose the word that completes the sentence and write it on the line.

1. Troy, Niles, and Lowell are three _____ places to live.
   (nice, nicest)

2. Troy is a _____ town than Lowell.
   (bigger, biggest)

3. Niles is the _____ town of the three.
   (bigger, biggest)

4. Of the three towns, Sal thinks Troy has the _____ people.
   (friendlier, friendliest)

5. Compared to Niles, he thinks Lowell has a _____ downtown.
   (prettier, prettiest)

6. The flowers downtown are the _____ he has ever seen.
   (prettier, prettiest)

7. All three towns have _____ high school football teams.
   (great, greatest)

8. This year, Niles was ranked _____ than Lowell.
   (higher, highest)

9. Niles was ranked _____ than Troy.
   (lower, lowest)

10. Troy had the _____ football team of the three towns.
    (better, best)

11. Sal would be _____ living in any one of the towns.
    (happy, happiest)

107

dirty   dirtier   dirtiest

1. We were washing our _____ car. The inside windows were the

_____ parts on the whole car. The hubcaps were even

_____ than they had been the last time we washed them.

---

large   larger   largest

2. The sales clerk showed me some _____ sweaters. They were

_____ than the ones I had at home. In fact they were the

_____ sweaters in the store.

---

hungry   hungrier   hungriest

3. Tad is the _____ boy I have ever known. He is usually

_____ at dinner than he was at lunch. But then, he is

_____ most of the time.

---

weak   weaker   weakest

4. The radio signals grew _____ as the evening wore on. They had

been quite _____ when the storm began. But they were the

_____ during the heaviest thunder and lightning.

---

early   earlier   earliest

5. José gets up the _____ of anyone in our class. Morrie thinks he

gets up _____, but even I get up _____ than he does.

LESSON 54: Suffixes -ER, -EST

Name _____

Rules The suffix **eer** usually means *someone who.* The suffixes **ee, ent,** and **ant** can also mean *someone who.* These suffixes can also mean *that which.*

EXAMPLES

Word	Definition
puppet**eer**	someone who works puppets
pay**ee**	someone who is paid
repell**ent**	that which repels
serv**ant**	someone who serves

Directions Read each sentence. Write a definition for the underlined word on the line below the sentence.

1. The current <u>occupants</u> are moving out of the apartment.

   Occupant means _____.

2. First they hired an <u>auctioneer</u> to sell some of their belongings.

   Auctioneer means _____.

3. Then they hired several <u>assistants</u> to help them move their other things.

   Assistant means _____.

4. The assistants are <u>employees</u> of the local moving company.

   Employee means _____.

5. The occupants voted in today's election by <u>absentee</u> ballot.

   Absentee means _____.

6. They wanted to be sure to get to vote for the new <u>president</u>.

   President means _____.

LESSON 55: Suffixes -EE, -EER, -ENT, -ANT

1. Ben is an _____ and will be driving a train out of town on election day.

auctioneer
engineer

2. Since he will be away, he is voting by _____ ballot.

absentee
payee

3. One of the issues on the ballot is especially _____ to Ben.

important
accountant

4. It will affect where his _____ go to school.

repellents
dependents

5. An _____ to the school board has suggested some school boundary changes.

appointee
payee

6. Ben is a _____ of one of the areas that would be affected.

precedent
resident

7. Therefore, he is an _____ of those who are proposing the change.

president
opponent

LESSON 55: Suffixes -EE, -EER, -ENT, -ANT

Name _____

Rules When added to a word to make an adjective, the suffix **ful** means *full of or having a tendency to.* When added to a word to make a noun, **ful** means *a certain amount.* The suffix **ness** means *the quality or condition of being.*

EXAMPLES

cheer + ful = cheerful, an adjective that means *full of cheer*

scoop + ful = scoopful, a noun that means *an amount the size of a scoop*

new + ness = newness, *the condition of being new*

Directions Choose one word from the box to complete each of the following sentences. Write the word on the line.

quietness	darkness	plentiful	successful	armful
spoonful	harmful	peaceful	coolness	sleepiness

1. Pat and Lynn chose a very _____ campsite.

2. Its _____ was a pleasant relief from the noise of the city.

3. Lynn found an _____ of logs for the campfire.

4. Pat was _____ in building a roaring fire.

5. It brought some light to the _____ of the campsite.

6. It helped them keep warm in the _____ of the evening.

7. It also helped keep away any _____ animals.

8. Lynn cooked some stew and scooped a _____ onto Pat's plate.

9. The stew was _____, so Pat had a second helping.

10. They sat and talked until _____ caused them to settle down for the night.

LESSON 56: Suffixes -FUL, -NESS

1. Deb asked her mother to _____ her plan her wedding.
   ○ help   ○ helped   ○ helpful

2. Deb wanted the most _____ wedding she could afford.
   ○ beauty   ○ beautify   ○ beautiful

3. She wanted all her friends to share in her _____.
   ○ happiness   ○ happier   ○ happy

4. Much _____ planning was necessary.
   ○ caring   ○ careful   ○ carefully

5. Her fiancé, Steve, was very _____ with the wedding plans.
   ○ help   ○ helpful   ○ helper

6. He made some _____ suggestions for the wedding ceremony.
   ○ use   ○ user   ○ useful

7. Deb's mother was impressed by Steve's _____.
   ○ thoughtful   ○ thoughtfulness ○ thoughtless

8. She began to see what a _____ person Steve was.
   ○ kind   ○ kinder   ○ kindness

9. She was _____ her daughter was marrying such a fine man.
   ○ glad   ○ gladly   ○ gladness

10. All of the planning had a _____ result.
    ○ success   ○ successful   ○ succession

11. Everyone who came to the wedding had a _____ time.
    ○ delight   ○ delighted   ○ delightful

12. Steve and Deb's _____ towards each other was obvious.
    ○ tenderly   ○ tenderness   ○ tender

13. Their wedding was the start of a _____ life together.
    ○ wonderful   ○ wondered   ○ wondering

Name _____

Directions Read the following letter. Circle each word that contains a suffix you have studied in this unit. You will circle 21 words. Then write each word you have circled. The suffixes you have studied are listed in the box.

er	or	ist	est	ee	eer	ent
ant	ward	en	ize	ful	ness	

Dearest Grandma:

I apologize for not writing sooner. We had a dreadful prairie storm many weeks ago, and I still get nervous whenever the wind begins to blow. The awesomeness of nature is overwhelming sometimes. The wildness of this new land is so different from our civilized city home back there with you.

We had a visitor last week. A doctor traveling westward spent several days with us. He is a specialist in troubles of the bones and gave Papa some excellent advice for his sore leg. Papa says he was far better than the doctor back home, whom he says is really only a profiteer.

Mama is busier every day with her orchard. The apples should start to ripen soon. I act as her assistant, but I'm afraid I have much to learn before I become a farmer.

Please do not not worry about us. You must realize that it is fun to be a resident of a new land. If we do not like it here, we can always move onward.

Love,
Charlotte

1. _____

2. _____

3. _____

4. _____

5. _____

6. _____

7. _____

8. _____

9. _____

10. _____

11. _____

12. _____

13. _____

14. _____

15. _____

16. _____

17. _____

18. _____

19. _____

20. _____

21. _____

Read the following short paragraphs. Then answer the questions below.

A. Buy the "Wrestler Body Building Kit." It will strengthen your body and make you stronger than anyone else. Move forward with "Wrestler."

B. Dear Editor:

Our city is the best because we have the best mayor. We are very proud that he is a nominee for governor. He is intelligent, cheerful, and helpful. Also, he is interested in our schools.

We do not look forward to losing such a good leader, but we hope our citizens will vote for Sam Brown for governor.

Sincerely yours,
Fifth Grade—Oak Valley School

C. Dear Sonia,

We are hopeful that you will be our visitor over the holidays. There will be a guitarist in town whom I think you would enjoy. Also, the art museum has an exhibit by your favorite painter. It is our busiest time at the store, but we will always make time for our delightful granddaughter.

Love,
Grandpa

---

1. What does Paragraph A try to persuade someone to do?

_____

2. What does Paragraph B try to persuade someone to do?

_____

3. What does Paragraph C try to persuade someone to do?

_____

Directions Write the words from the paragraphs that have the suffixes **or, ward,** or **ful.**

_____   _____   _____

_____   _____   _____

_____   _____   _____

Name _____

Rule The suffixes **hood**, **ship**, and **ment** usually mean *the state or condition of being.*

EXAMPLES

Suffix	Word	Definition
hood	child**hood**	the state or condition of being a child
ship	leader**ship**	the state or condition of being a leader
ment	retire**ment**	the state or condition of being retired

Directions Read the following paragraph. Circle each word that has the suffix **hood, ship,** or **ment.**

Our neighborhood track team won the championship this fall. There was a lot of excitement over this accomplishment. The township has even talked about the likelihood of buying trophies for the members of the team. The leadership of Matt Evans is one factor in the team's improvement this season. There is surely no argument about that!

Directions Now write the correct circled word on the line next to its definition.

1. something done well _____

2. place where people live _____ or

   _____

3. probability _____

4. something that has gotten better _____

5. quarrel _____

6. first place position _____

7. great thrill _____

8. guidance, direction _____

Directions Add the suffix **hood, ship,** or **ment** to each word below to form a new word. Write the new word on the line.

1. child _____

2. likely _____

3. relation _____

4. equip _____

5. hard _____

6. enjoy _____

7. author _____

8. retire _____

Directions Write one of the words you made above to complete each of the following sentences.

1. Since Grandpa's _____, he and Juan do many things together.

2. Juan and Grandpa had always had a good _____.

3. Grandpa enjoyed telling Juan stories of his _____.

4. He told of learning to use heavy farm _____ as a child.

5. Juan and Grandpa share the _____ of a story they wrote.

6. It is about the _____ of a young boy growing up on a farm.

7. There is not much _____ of the story ever being published.

8. What is important is the _____ they got from writing it!

LESSON 58: Suffixes -HOOD, -SHIP, -MENT

Name _____

Rule The suffixes **able** and **ible** usually mean *able to be* or *full of*.

EXAMPLES

Suffix	Word	Definition
able	wash**able**	able to be washed
ible	sens**ible**	full of sense

Directions Choose the correct word from the box to complete each sentence, and write it on the line. Notice that when the base word ends in **e** or **y**, these letters are dropped before the suffix is added.

reliable	reversible	washable	collapsible	reducible
profitable	breakable	readable	eatable	defensible

1. Clothing that can be cleaned at home is _____.

2. Something that can be made smaller is _____.

3. An activity that makes a lot of money is _____.

4. Something that can be damaged if it is dropped is _____.

5. A jacket that can be worn with either side out is _____.

6. Food that is not spoiled is _____.

7. Something that can be read is _____.

8. Something that can be defended is _____.

9. Something that can be relied on is _____.

10. Something that can be taken apart and put in a smaller package is

_____.

1. Joe has a shiny, red convertible. _____

2. Driving it is very enjoyable for him. _____

3. His mom wishes he had a more sensible car. _____

4. Her attitude toward the car is not very favorable. _____

5. Joe keeps telling her what a likable car it is. _____

6. He says he is a very responsible driver. _____

7. It is not conceivable to her that he could love that car. _____

8. Joe's reasons for having the car are defensible. _____

9. In the first place, he finds the car adorable. _____

10. It is also a comfortable car to drive. _____

11. It is usable year-round with the top up. _____

12. The car's controls are very accessible. _____

13. On these points, his mom is agreeable. _____

Name _____

Rule The suffixes **ion**, **ation**, and **ition** usually mean *the act of* or *the condition of being*.

EXAMPLES

Suffix	Word	Definition
ion	exhaus**tion**	the condition of being exhausted
ation	invit**ation**	the act of inviting
ition	add**ition**	the act of adding

Directions Read each sentence and the two words below the line. Choose the word that best completes the sentence and write it on the line.

1. Beth has _____ a ticket for the computer show.
   (reserved, reservation)

2. She wants to see the new software _____.
   (demonstrate, demonstration)

3. The software she wants is for a new _____ program.
   (add, addition)

4. The _____ is at ten o'clock.
   (presentation, present)

5. There is a large _____ of software at the show.
   (select, selection)

6. Beth sees software that is used to _____ music.
   (compose, composition)

7. She also sees software that does _____.
   (illustrations, illustrates)

8. She even _____ some software that talks.
   (inspects, inspections)

9. By the end of the show, Beth suffers from _____.
   (exhausted, exhaustion)

119

EXAMPLES

Base Word	Suffix	New Word
elate	ion	elation
realize	ation	realization
compose	ition	composition

Directions   Add the suffix **ion**, **ition**, or **ation** to each word below to form a new word. Write the new word on the line.

1. concentrate _____   2. define _____

3. confirm _____   4. celebrate _____

5. rotate _____   6. imagine _____

7. compete _____   8. invite _____

9. exhibit _____   10. inspect _____

11. quote _____   12. add _____

Directions   Write one of the words you made above to complete each of the following sentences.

1. Lance will perform in the big diving _____ today.

2. The _____ will be strong with many good divers.

3. Each diver will do ten dives, one in each _____ .

4. Lance is waiting for _____ of when he will dive.

5. Before he dives, he gives the diving board a good _____ .

6. He wonders what the judges' _____ of a good dive is.

7. Lance must keep his _____ in order to dive well.

8. When Lance wins the event, his family has a big _____ .

9. Then Lance gets an _____ to join the best diving team.

10. Even in his _____ , he'd never expected to be so good.

11. Lance will be an _____ to any diving team.

LESSON 60: Suffixes -ION, -ATION, -ITION

Name _____

Rules The suffixes **ance**, **ence**, and **ity** usually mean *the quality or state of being*. The suffix **ive** usually means *likely to or having to do with.*

EXAMPLES

Suffix	Word	Definition
ance	import**ance**	the quality of being important
ence	depend**ence**	the quality of being dependent
ity	real**ity**	the quality of being real
ive	impress**ive**	likely to impress

Directions Write the base word and the suffix that were combined to make each of the following words.

1. personality = _____ + _____

2. confidence = _____ + _____

3. impressive = _____ + _____

4. acceptance = _____ + _____

5. active = _____ + _____

6. sincerity = _____ + _____

7. creative = _____ + _____

Directions Use the words above in the sentences.

1. Tanya is always busy because she is _____ in so many groups.

2. She has an outgoing _____ and is very friendly.

3. She is a very caring person and shows it by her _____.

4. She always has good ideas because she is so _____.

5. Other group members have great _____ in Tanya's skills.

6. Whatever Tanya is in charge of always ends up being _____.

7. This year, Tanya won an award and gave a fine _____ speech.

LESSON 61: Suffixes -ANCE, -ENCE, -IVE, -ITY

Definition An **analogy** tells the relationship that one thing has to another thing.

EXAMPLES
Car is to **garage** as **airplane** is to **hangar**.
Kitten is to **cat** as **puppy** is to **dog**.
Huge is to **massive** as **honesty** is to **sincerity**.

Directions Circle the correct word to complete each analogy. Then write the word.

1. **Dynamite** is to **explosive** as **tape** is to _____ .

   adhesive   impressive   selective

2. **Helping** is to **assistance** as **watching** is to _____ .

   hindrance   observance   coincidence

3. **Negative** is to **positive** as **criminality** is to _____ .

   simplicity   complexity   legality

4. **Dance** is to **activity** as **uproar** is to _____ .

   disturbance   attendance   guidance

5. **Insecurity** is to **confidence** as **sameness** is to _____ .

   residence   conference   difference

6. **Leading** is to **guidance** as **forgiving** is to _____ .

   insurance   tolerance   observance

7. **Offensive** is to **defensive** as **superiority** is to _____ .

   security   inferiority   popularity

8. **Unusual** is to **distinctive** as **pretty** is to _____ .

   attractive   selective   executive

9. **Advertisement** is to **publicity** as **generator** is to _____ .

   mortality   electricity   legality

LESSON 61: Suffixes -ANCE, -ENCE, -IVE, -ITY

Name _____

Directions   Read the letter. Draw a line under each word that has one of the suffixes in the box. Then circle the suffix. You will underline fifteen words.

Suffixes			
hood	ion	ance	ive
ship	ation	ence	able
ment	ition	ity	ible

Dear Molly,

   We want you to visit us soon. We are getting ready for a big celebration on the Fourth of July in honor of Independence Day. The whole neighborhood is involved in the preparation. Each street is responsible for one float. There will be a prize for the float that shows the most creativity and imagination. Some look impressive already. It is conceivable that ours will receive special recognition.

   The parade will begin at noon. There will be police clearance all along the parade route to Settlement Park. There will be games and plenty of refreshments available at the park.

   I hope you can join us to have some fun and to renew our friendship.

                                        Yours truly,

                                        Diana

Directions Put a check mark in front of the topic that you would like to write about.

Definition Persuasion is trying to convince someone to do something or think a certain way. The topics below all are examples of persuasion.

_____ persuading someone to buy something

_____ convincing a classmate to study harder

_____ convincing someone to give up eating junk food

_____ making up an advertisement telling why a certain product is good for dogs or cats

_____ convincing a friend to participate in a sport

_____ _____
                              (my idea)

Directions Do some persuasive writing about your topic. Clearly state your opinion and explain your reasons for it. Use at least three words with suffixes you have learned about in this unit. Circle the words. Proofread your writing.

_____

_____

_____

_____

_____

_____

_____

_____

_____

_____

_____

_____

_____

_____

_____

LESSON 62: Review and write

Name _____

Directions Form new words by combining each base word and suffix. Write the new words on the lines.

Rule If a short-vowel word ends in a single consonant, double the consonant before adding a suffix that begins with a vowel.

1. rub + ing _____

2. laugh + ing _____

3. jog + ing _____

4. quick + est _____

5. rob + er _____

6. chap + ed _____

7. start + ing _____

8. strut + ed _____

9. hit + er _____

10. fat + est _____

11. plan + ing _____

12. stun + ed _____

13. fast + er _____

14. skid + ed _____

Directions Read each sentence and circle the correct suffix in parentheses. Write the new word on the line.

1. I think holidays are the great (er/est) days of the year. _____

2. I clap (est/ed) loudly at the Fourth of July celebration. _____

3. Crowds jam (est/ed) the roads for the Thanksgiving parade. _____

4. Government lead (ers/ing) marched in the parade. _____

5. Plan (ed/ing) the annual Memorial Day picnic was fun. _____

6. Chat (ing/er) with friends is my favorite holiday pastime. _____

LESSON 63: Words that double the final consonant to add a suffix

Directions Circle each suffix below that begins with a vowel. Form new words by putting each base word and suffix together. Write the new words on the lines.

1. scan + ing _____
2. fast + est _____
3. hot + est _____
4. sad + ness _____
5. steep + er _____
6. plot + ed _____
7. equip + ment _____
8. hard + ness _____
9. drip + ed _____
10. snap + ing _____
11. heart + less _____
12. wet + est _____
13. cram + ed _____
14. cheer + ful _____
15. rapid + ly _____
16. strap + ed _____

Directions Circle the base word in each word in the box. Then complete each sentence with a word from the box.

throbbing	quitters	slipped	shredded
flopping	flippers	squatted	swimmer
raining	trapper	hottest	dimmest

1. We swam in the pool on the _____ day of the summer.

2. While I swam, I wore a face mask and _____.

3. I almost _____ when I walked onto the diving board.

4. We held a race to determine the fastest _____.

5. Our muscles were _____ from so much swimming.

6. If it isn't _____ tomorrow, we'll go swimming again.

LESSON 63: Words that double the final consonant to add a suffix

Name _____

Directions Form new words by adding the correct suffixes.

Hint When a word ends in final **e**, drop the **e** before adding a suffix that begins with a vowel.

	es	ed	ing
1. squeeze	_____	_____	_____
2. disapprove	_____	_____	_____
3. bribe	_____	_____	_____
4. hope	_____	_____	_____
5. imagine	_____	_____	_____

	er	est
6. late	_____	_____
7. little	_____	_____
8. humble	_____	_____
9. nice	_____	_____
10. strange	_____	_____

Directions Write the base word for each of the following words.

1. cradles	_____	2. approved	_____
3. observer	_____	4. pavement	_____
5. latest	_____	6. grazing	_____
7. sprinkler	_____	8. changed	_____
9. scraping	_____	10. safest	_____
11. decided	_____	12. combining	_____
13. trader	_____	14. scrambled	_____
15. candles	_____	16. hiking	_____

127

Rule   When a word ends in **e**, drop the **e** before adding a suffix that begins with a vowel.

ing	ion	ment	ness	ed
able	ful	less	ers	

1. Theories about _____ rain have existed for centuries.
    (make)

2. Early attempts were _____ on superstition.
    (base)

3. Modern scientists have tried almost every method _____.
    (imagine)

4. The _____ of the atmosphere is a major factor.
    (cold)

5. Supercooled clouds exist at temperatures below _____.
    (freeze)

6. _____ of the air was first proposed in 1891.
    (Refrigerate)

7. _____ to this idea might think it is impossible.
    (Strange)

8. It is generally _____ that this method does not work.
    (believe)

9. "Rain makers" are _____ without good evidence.
    (defense)

10. Scientists are _____ that a method will be found.
    (hope)

Name _____

Directions Many words have more than one suffix. Read each word in the box. Underline the first suffix and circle the second suffix.

Hint Remember that **s** can be a suffix.

1. watchfully
2. Amazingly
3. painlessly
4. migrations
5. carelessness
6. widening
7. publications
8. frightfulness
9. enlightening
10. attractions
11. thoughtfulness
12. powerlessness
13. increasingly
14. cheerfulness
15. joyfully
16. hopefully

Directions Use the words from above to complete each sentence. Write the word on the line.

1. Tracking migrating birds is becoming _____ popular.

2. The _____ of many birds take place in the spring and fall.

3. _____ , some birds return to the same fields every year.

4. Studying migrating birds can be an _____ experience.

5. There are many _____ about birds.

6. Human _____ has blocked some migration paths.

7. The _____ of some groups has helped to protect birds.

8. Bird lovers watch the sky _____ every year.

1. I was awakened today by an annoyingly sore throat.

   _____ _____

2. I thankfully agreed to have my tonsils painlessly removed.

   _____ _____

3. My heartbeat quickened as I fearfully entered the hospital.

   _____ _____

4. "I perform these operations carefully," the doctor said.

   _____ _____

5. The doctor's cheerfulness heartened me.

   _____ _____

6. The doctor worked effortlessly as I slept peacefully.

   _____ _____

7. My heart lightened as the assistants wheeled me to my room.

   _____ _____

8. Widening my mouth, I joyfully ate some ice cream.

   _____ _____

Directions Circle each base word from the sentences above in the puzzle. The words may be written across, up and down, or diagonally. Some words are backwards.

```
O E I H E J K N A H T H
I P E A K O P S E I O E
N A E B A Y E Q C A A A
A I I R W P C Z W E E R
N N J I A O E F F O R T
N N I A S T A P E T E H
O E P S S I E U A R C G
Y G C W I D E C R X A I
R M A O S G F U H D E L
A O R W T R Z M T H P D
C H E E R K B Q U I C K
```

130

LESSON 65: Words with more than one suffix

Name _____

Rule If a word ends in **y** preceded by a consonant, change the **y** to **i** before adding a suffix. If **y** is preceded by a vowel, just add the suffix.

EXAMPLES

Singular	Plural
activity	activities
chimney	chimneys

Directions Add **s** or **es** to write the plural form of each word.

1. story _____

2. canary _____

3. company _____

4. decoy _____

5. country _____

6. army _____

7. donkey _____

8. injury _____

9. victory _____

10. bay _____

11. holiday _____

12. missionary _____

13. valley _____

14. library _____

15. mystery _____

Directions Write the base word ending in **y** of each word below.

1. peppiest _____

2. dustier _____

3. mutinied _____

4. keyed _____

5. worrying _____

6. tardiest _____

7. rustier _____

8. flies _____

9. obeys _____

10. luckiest _____

11. fancier _____

12. multiplying _____

13. relayed _____

14. carried _____

LESSON 66: Adding suffixes to words ending in Y

Hint Remember the rules for adding suffixes to words ending in **y.**

1. lucky + er _____

2. greasy + est _____

3. worry + ed _____

4. easy + er _____

5. obey + s _____

6. occupy + ed _____

7. sleepy + est _____

8. busy + er _____

9. salty + er _____

10. toy + ed _____

11. fancy + est _____

12. heavy + er _____

Directions Use the words you formed to complete the sentences. Then, write the circled letters from the answers in order, and you will find the answer to the riddle.

Riddle: What is the best material for kites?

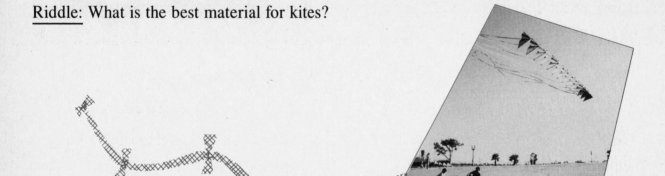

1. Cinderella had the Ⓞ _ _ _ _ _ _ _ gown at the ball.

2. One little pig was Ⓞ _ _ _ _ _ _ than the other two.

3. Jack shouldn't have _ _ Ⓞ _ _ with the magic beans.

4. Hansel and Gretel visited a house _ _ _ _ Ⓞ _ _ _ by a witch.

5. Babe, the blue ox, made Paul Bunyan's work _ Ⓞ _ _ _ _ _.

6. Rip Van Winkle is the _ _ _ _ Ⓞ _ _ _ _ character in any book.

7. The Brothers Grimm were _ _ _ _ Ⓞ _ than other authors.

8. The seven dwarfs _ _ Ⓞ _ _ _ _ about Snow White.

Riddle answer: _ _ _ _ _ _ _ _ _

132

LESSON 66: Adding suffixes to words ending in Y

Name _____

Rules If a word ends in **y** preceded by a consonant, change the **y** to **i** when adding **ly**. If the **y** is preceded by a vowel, add **ly**. If a word ends in **le**, the **le** is dropped.

EXAMPLES

heavy + ly = heavily
coy + ly = coyly
wobble + ly = wobbly

Directions Add **ly** to each word. Write the new word on the line.

1. noisy _____
2. coy _____
3. drizzle _____
4. greedy _____
5. bubble _____
6. dizzy _____
7. hasty _____
8. wiggle _____
9. merry _____
10. pebble _____
11. probable _____
12. lucky _____

Directions Complete each sentence with a word from above.

1. It was a _____ day, perfect for a trip to the indoor aquarium.

2. The aquarium was enormous, so we _____ viewed each exhibit.

3. The bottom of the aquarium was _____, and not covered with sand.

4. The diver's air tanks made the water _____.

5. The _____ arms of the squid grabbed everything in sight.

6. _____, the glass walls stopped it from grabbing us.

7. We _____ watched the dolphins swim round and round.

8. I'll _____ go back to the aquarium at least twice a year.

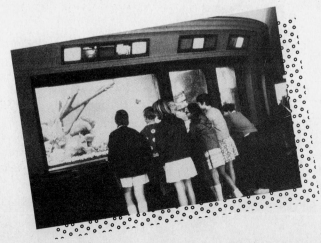

LESSON 67: Adding suffix -LY to words ending in Y or LE

1. Eating _____ every day helps an athlete keep fit.
   (healthy)

2. A trainer should _____ supervise every workout.
   (reliable)

3. Proper training techniques can prevent _____ injury.
   (body)

4. Training _____ will not help an athlete.
   (lazy)

5. Jogging can strengthen _____ legs.
   (wobble)

6. If athletes practice _____, they will perform poorly.
   (sloppy)

7. Athletes should not begin weight training _____.
   (hasty)

8. _____, many athletes are born with coordination.
   (Lucky)

9. Athletes in good shape can do exercises _____.
   (easy)

10. Sometimes athletes should _____ take a day off from training.
    (happy)

11. Gymnasts can move _____ on the parallel bars.
    (nimble)

12. Athletes should accept both victory and defeat _____.
    (noble)

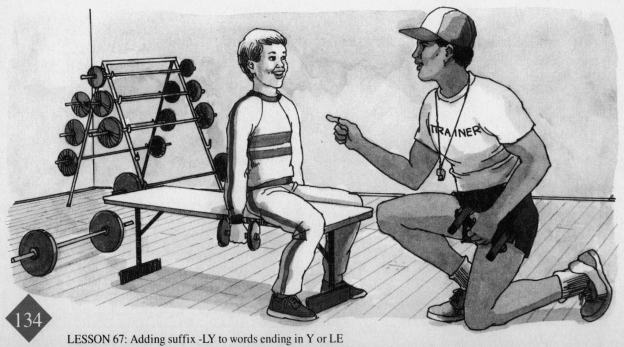

LESSON 67: Adding suffix -LY to words ending in Y or LE

Name _____

Directions Add the suffixes to the base words to form new words. Complete the story on this page by writing the new words on the lines.

Two Unique Inventors

Throughout history, the _____ of people has
(invent + ive + ness)

_____ many _____ _____.
(produce + ed)   (amaze + ing)   (accomplish + ments)

Consider Levi Hutchins, a clockmaker who _____ during the 1700s.
(live + ed)

He worked _____ every day and seldom _____
(busy + ly)   (waste + ed)

time. Levi _____ to rise at 4 a.m. each day. Not
(try + ed)

_____, he sometimes overslept. This greatly
(surprise + ing + ly)

_____ Levi.
(annoy + ed)

One day, the idea of _____ an alarm clock struck Levi. His
(make + ing)

_____ worked _____ and
(invent + ion)   (simple + ly)

_____. Ever after, Levi was _____ at 4 a.m. He
(success + ful + ly)   (awake + en + ed)

never _____ for a patent. Money was _____
(apply + ed)   (seem + ing + ly)

unimportant to him.

Harvey Kennedy, on the other hand, _____ benefited from his
(profit + able + ly)

_____. He invented the shoelace, and made two and one-half million
(ability + es)

dollars.

People bought it _____ because they were
(immediate + ly)

_____ of _____, _____, and
(tire + ed)   (pin + ing)   (strap + ing)

_____ their shoes.
(buckle + ing)

Directions   Write **T** if the statement is **true.** Write **F** if it is **false.**

1. ____   Inventors' abilities help others.

2. ____   Levi Hutchins avoided hard work.

3. ____   Levi hated to oversleep.

4. ____   Levi made an alarm clock that worked.

5. ____   Levi made lots of money on his invention.

6. ____   Harvey Kennedy never applied for a patent.

7. ____   Harvey Kennedy invented the shoelace.

8. ____   Before the shoelace, people had to pin, strap, or buckle their shoes.

9. ____   It took a long time for Harvey's invention to catch on.

Directions   Outlines help you summarize an article for study or prepare a speech. An outline may be written in question-and-answer form. Complete the outline below for the stories of the two inventors. The outline will present the main facts. One answer is filled in for you. Fill in the rest of the answers to finish the outline.

Title   Two Unique Inventors

First
Heading   I.   Levi Hutchins

      A.   What invented? _____ alarm clock _____

      B.   Why? _____

      C.   How did he benefit? _____

Second
Heading   II.   Harvey Kennedy

      A.   What invented? _____

      B.   Why did people like it? _____

          _____

      C.   How much did he make? _____

          _____

LESSON 68: Review and write

Name _____

Rule If a word ends in **f** or **fe**, the **f** or **fe** is changed to **v** and **es** is added to form the plural. A word that ends in **ff** is made plural by adding **s**. Exceptions are *chief*, *belief*, *reef*, and *roof*.

EXAMPLES

Singular	Plural
wolf	wolves
cliff	cliffs
chief	chiefs

Directions Fill in the circle under the word that completes each sentence.

1. Ranchers spent much of their ____ moving cattle.

   lives lifes lifves
   ○   ○   ○

2. Their ____ often helped with the daily roundup.

   wifes wives wiffes
   ○   ○   ○

3. The cowboys carried buck ____.

   knives knifes kniffs
   ○   ○   ○

4. They wore ____ to protect their faces in dust storms.

   scarfs scarves scarfes
   ○   ○   ○

5. The cowboys used dried ____ as fuel for campfires.

   leafes leafs leaves
   ○   ○   ○

6. They traveled with a cook who baked ____ of bread.

   loafs loaves loafes
   ○   ○   ○

7. Mountain ____ stopped the herds from stampeding.

   cliffes cliffs clives
   ○   ○   ○

8. Sometimes the ____ were very steep.

   bluffs bluffes bluves
   ○   ○   ○

9. The young ____ often fell behind the herd.

   calfs calves calfes
   ○   ○   ○

10. Injured ____ could slow the horses down.

    hooves hoofs hoofes
    ○   ○   ○

11. Tribal ____ usually allowed the herds to pass.

    chiefes chieves chiefs
    ○   ○   ○

12. Packs of ____ sometimes attacked the herds.

    wolfes wolves wolfs
    ○   ○   ○

13. Cattle ____ called rustlers were also a problem.

    thiefes thieves thiefs
    ○   ○   ○

1. belief _____
2. calf _____
3. dwarf _____
4. half _____
5. knife _____
6. whiff _____
7. cuff _____
8. wife _____
9. chief _____
10. life _____
11. staff _____
12. loaf _____
13. scarf _____
14. shelf _____
15. thief _____

Directions   Use the plural words you wrote to answer the questions below.

1. Who are leaders of tribes? _____

2. Which are kitchen tools used to cut and slice? _____

3. What are the shapes that breads come in? _____

4. On what can you place books? _____

5. Which two of these make one whole? _____

6. What does a cat supposedly have nine of? _____

7. What do you call young cattle? _____

8. What do you call ideas you think are true or real? _____

9. Who are the partners of husbands? _____

10. What can people wear on their head and tie under their chin? _____

LESSON 69: Plural form for words ending in F and FE

Name _____

Rule If a word ends in **o**, add **s** to form the plural. Some words ending in **o** form the plural by adding **es**.

EXAMPLES

potato — potatoes
tomato — tomatoes
buffalo — buffaloes
tornado — tornadoes

Directions Write the plural of each word.

1. banjo _____
2. poncho _____
3. piccolo _____
4. patio _____
5. echo _____
6. hero _____
7. solo _____
8. radio _____
9. cello _____
10. rodeo _____
11. piano _____
12. tempo _____

Directions Complete each sentence using a plural from the exercise above.

1. Our music teacher told us to bring our _____ to class.

2. We were studying elements of music, such as rhythms and _____ .

3. The sound of twenty radios sent _____ through the classroom.

4. We learned that _____ are not used in symphony orchestras.

5. _____ look like violins, but are much bigger.

6. There are eighty-eight keys on grand _____ .

7. We listened to _____ and guessed which instrument was playing.

8. We could easily hear the shrill notes of the small _____ .

LESSON 70: Plural form for words ending in O

Directions   Write the plural form of each word.

1. piano _____   2. alto _____

3. photo _____   4. igloo _____

5. piccolo _____   6. tornado _____

7. poncho _____   8. avocado _____

9. tomato _____   10. hero _____

11. banjo _____   12. cello _____

13. patio _____   14. rodeo _____

15. potato _____   16. kangaroo _____

Directions   Use the plural words you wrote to answer the questions below.

1. Which words name musical instruments?

_____ _____ _____ _____

2. What are cowboy and cowgirl contests called? _____

3. Which kind of vegetable tastes good in all these forms: mashed, French fried, baked, and

scalloped? _____

4. What are terrible wind storms called? _____

5. What are people called who do brave and wonderful deeds? _____

6. Which vegetables are used to make spaghetti sauce and ketchup? _____

7. What are pictures that have been taken with a camera called? _____

8. What are large, waterproof cloaks often worn by campers? _____

9. What are dome-shaped huts made of snow? _____

10. What are outdoor courtyards? _____

LESSON 70: Plural form for words ending in O

Name _____

Directions These words are the same in their singular and plural forms. If the word names a plant or a food that comes from a plant, write **P**. If it names an animal or food that comes from an animal, write **A**.

Hint Some words do not change at all in their plural form.

1. ___ spinach
2. ___ moose
3. ___ cattle
4. ___ deer
5. ___ rye
6. ___ butter
7. ___ fish
8. ___ milk
9. ___ sheep
10. ___ broccoli
11. ___ popcorn
12. ___ bacon
13. ___ sauerkraut
14. ___ oatmeal
15. ___ salmon
16. ___ spaghetti
17. ___ trout
18. ___ honey
19. ___ cod
20. ___ zucchini
21. ___ shrimp
22. ___ haddock
23. ___ bread
24. ___ wheat

Directions Read each word and find its plural form in the box. Next choose a word from the box and write it beside its definition. Its singular form is in parentheses.

Hint Some words change completely in their plural form. Some other plural forms may not be familiar to you. They do not follow any of the rules.

women	geese	alumni	feet
fungi	oases	children	mice
teeth	men	oxen	crises

1. foot _____
2. man _____
3. child _____
4. woman _____
5. goose _____
6. mouse _____
7. ox _____
8. tooth _____

9. _____ times of danger or anxious waiting (crisis)

10. _____ people who have attended a school (alumnus)

11. _____ plants such as mushrooms, toadstools, and molds (fungus)

12. _____ places in the desert where there is water (oasis)

141

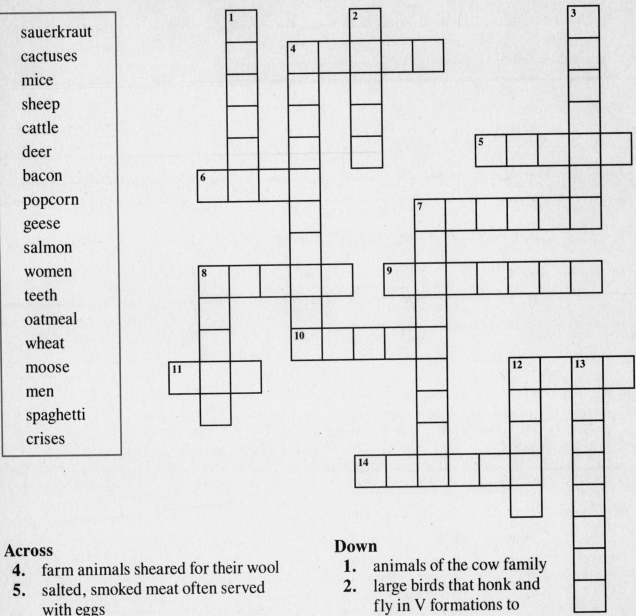

sauerkraut
cactuses
mice
sheep
cattle
deer
bacon
popcorn
geese
salmon
women
teeth
oatmeal
wheat
moose
men
spaghetti
crises

Across

4. farm animals sheared for their wool
5. salted, smoked meat often served with eggs
6. swift animals living in the woods
7. large ocean fish that swim up rivers to lay their eggs
8. cereal grasses used for making flour
9. cooked cereal made from ground, boiled oats
10. what you use to bite and chew food
11. more than one male
12. small rodents found in houses and fields
14. stressful, anxious times

Down

1. animals of the cow family
2. large birds that honk and fly in V formations to migrate
3. corn that turns into white puffs when heated
4. cabbage that's spiced and tastes sour
7. Italian dish made with pasta and tomato sauce
8. more than one female
12. large woodland animals with wide antlers
13. prickly plants you wouldn't want to sit on

LESSON 71: Other plural forms

Name _____

Remember these rules for dividing words into syllables.

Double vowels stand for only one vowel sound. (inst**ea**d, sp**oo**nful)

A prefix or suffix is a syllable in itself if it contains a vowel sound. (**pre**wash, old**en**)

Some prefixes and suffixes have more than one syllable. (**ultra**fine, **super**human)

		Vowels Seen	Vowel Sounds	Syllables			Vowels Seen	Vowel Sounds	Syllables
1.	congratulations	___	___	___	19.	insight	___	___	___
2.	encountered	___	___	___	20.	exclamation	___	___	___
3.	exaggerating	___	___	___	21.	kangaroos	___	___	___
4.	irresponsible	___	___	___	22.	excitably	___	___	___
5.	determination	___	___	___	23.	handkerchiefs	___	___	___
6.	indirectly	___	___	___	24.	irritability	___	___	___
7.	invisible	___	___	___	25.	resolution	___	___	___
8.	foreshadows	___	___	___	26.	pavement	___	___	___
9.	imprisoned	___	___	___	27.	organizations	___	___	___
10.	illogical	___	___	___	28.	squeezing	___	___	___
11.	torpedoes	___	___	___	29.	scrubber	___	___	___
12.	motionless	___	___	___	30.	noisiest	___	___	___
13.	quickened	___	___	___	31.	sleepily	___	___	___
14.	observer	___	___	___	32.	entrusting	___	___	___
15.	combinations	___	___	___	33.	feebly	___	___	___
16.	neighborhood	___	___	___	34.	audible	___	___	___
17.	imagination	___	___	___	35.	overcook	___	___	___
18.	peaceful	___	___	___	36.	weighed	___	___	___

143

```
P C F C A C T U S E S Z
O A T M E A L J M N P R
P B C S W V E H O N E Y
C U D P A I R L A U P E
O T E A B C H E R O E S
R T F G P I C C O L O S
N E H H M I Y D A S A C
G R D E E R A P U H V E
L G K T E E T O C E E A
C O R T O M A T O E S L
C Z A I D Z O A L P E U
M A P B C A T T L E O M
S H R I M P E O B T K N
G U O Z O B E E S R S I
M Z T O A E L S B M N O
```

Rule Divide a compound word between the words that form the compound word.

EXAMPLES

| ear/drum | hand/bag | spell/down |
| snow/flake | house/boat | sun/shine |

Directions Underline the compound words in the sentences. Then divide them into syllables by drawing vertical lines between the words.

1. We must help safeguard the wildlife in national parks.
2. Respect for animals and plantlife should be a lifelong effort.
3. Highways that run through parklands destroy valuable land.
4. Landfills and airports near parks are dangerous to animals.
5. We should set aside park wetlands and backwoods just for animals.
6. Without laws and guidelines, some animals might become extinct.

Directions Write these words on the lines below. Use vertical lines to divide them into syllables.

Rule When a word ends in **le** preceded by a consonant, divide the word before that consonant.

cradle	angle	bottle	paddle	puzzle	ample
grumble	crumble	noble	gentle	handle	poodle
baffle	purple	mumble	fiddle	cripple	jungle
people	wobble	battle	dimple	fumble	startle

_____ cra|dle _____

_____ _____ _____

_____ _____ _____

_____ _____ _____

_____ _____ _____

_____ _____ _____

_____ _____ _____

Hint A word has as many syllables as it has vowel sounds. Some prefixes and suffixes can have more than one syllable.

1. protest _____ _____
2. wondering _____ _____
3. famous _____ _____
4. watermelon _____ _____
5. insects _____ _____
6. sofa _____ _____
7. strawberries _____ _____
8. startle _____ _____
9. wiggle _____ _____
10. skyscraper _____ _____
11. tablespoon _____ _____
12. prisons _____ _____
13. wintertime _____ _____
14. windowpane _____ _____
15. shopkeeper _____ _____
16. shipmate _____ _____
17. stepladder _____ _____
18. hunger _____ _____
19. taxation _____ _____
20. recess _____ _____
21. sudden _____ _____
22. whistle _____ _____
23. poodle _____ _____
24. giggled _____ _____
25. butterfly _____ _____

LESSON 73: Syllabicating compound words and words with prefixes and suffixes

Name _____

Directions Read the article. Complete each unfinished sentence by writing the plural form of each word on the line above it.

Sequoyah: Cherokee Hero

There were many famous Indian _____ in North America. Among the
chief

most famous is a Cherokee brave named Sequoyah. He had noticed white

_____ and _____ reading. He called their papers "talking
man   woman

_____." Members of his tribe held the _____ that reading
leaf   belief

was a gift of the Great Spirit and that it was not a human discovery. Sequoyah disagreed.

"You _____ could read if there was a way to write our language," he said.
yourself

For years, Sequoyah worked at figuring out signs for the sounds he heard. He wrote them

with _____ in bark, or with sticks on dirt. He received only
knife

_____ from his tribe. His own wife, like all the other
rebuff

_____ in the tribe, thought he was foolish. Yet, Sequoyah enriched the
wife

_____ of the Cherokee Indians. After twelve years, he had invented a simple
life

Cherokee alphabet. Within a few days, almost all _____,
man

_____, and _____ in the tribe could read!
woman   child

Sequoyah became one of the great _____ of the Cherokee nation. There
hero

are no _____ of Sequoyah, but a painting of him survives today.
photo

Plains Indians

The Indians of the High Plains were always on the move. They set up no permanent villages because they needed to keep on the move in search of buffaloes. Their homes were portable tepees—poles covered with hides. The arrival of the wild horse on the plains made life much easier for the Plains hunters. Braves became some of the best horseback riders in the world.

The Plains Indians had several uses for the buffaloes they hunted. They used the hides to cover their homes. The fur was used for blankets. They ate the animals' meat.

1. What is the article about?

   Plains Indians   Cherokees   Buffaloes

2. What is the first paragraph about?

   how they lived   how they worshipped

3. What is the second paragraph about?

   uses of the buffaloes   hunting the buffaloes

4. Why were their lives unsettled?

   moved searching buffaloes   moved finding farmland

5. What kinds of shelter did they have?

   tepee homes   long houses

6. What did the arrival of wild horses cause the Plains Indians to become?

   good farmers   excellent horseback riders

Directions Now use the answers you circled to complete the outline below.

Rule An **outline** helps you summarize the important ideas in a story or article. A **topic outline** is written with simple words or short phrases.

Title _____
        (Answer to Question 1)

First   I. _____
Heading   (Answer to Question 2)

         A. _____
            (Answer to Question 4)

         B. _____
            (Answer to Question 5)

         C. _____
            (Answer to Question 6)

LESSON 74: Review and write

Name _____

Directions Number the words in each column to show the alphabetical order.

Rule When words begin with the same letter or letters, look at the second or third letter to put the words in alphabetical order.

1.

payment _____

position _____

planter _____

pension _____

prance _____

2.

swaying _____

strawberry _____

seashore _____

skateboard _____

sickness _____

3.

awkward _____

arrive _____

amount _____

application _____

aching _____

4.

crayon _____

creek _____

crusty _____

cringe _____

crock _____

5.

lotion _____

loneliness _____

locust _____

loaves _____

loyalty _____

6.

southerly _____

sorrow _____

socialize _____

sometime _____

softening _____

7.

blond _____

battery _____

blanket _____

bugle _____

beach _____

8.

thaw _____

trio _____

tunnel _____

tumble _____

talent _____

9.

mistake _____

middle _____

microphone _____

mystery _____

morning _____

149

1.

belt/bind   open
mine/moon   stand
olive/ox   moan
quack/quietly   bend
stamp/star   quick

2.

back/bag   basket
baseball/battle   blink
beat/better   badge
blanket/block   bother
bonnet/bought   begin

1. **a/aid**
afraid
about
ache
also
address

2. **each/east**
easel
eagle
eat
ear
ease

3. **ladder/let**
last
list
lead
lamp
leap

4. **dear/dish**
deliver
deep
ditch
destroy
dimple

5. **imagine/increase**
indeed
immediately
imitate
include
incident

6. **stage/storage**
still
steep
stung
stick
stand

Name _____

Directions Study the pronunciation key. Then follow the directions below.

Hint The **respelling** that follows a dictionary entry shows how to pronounce that word. Use the dictionary's pronunciation key to help you pronounce each respelling.

VOWELS

SYMBOL	KEY WORDS	SYMBOL	KEY WORDS
a	ask, fat	ೲ	look, pull
ā	ape, date	ōō	ooze, tool
ä	car, lot	yೲ	unite, cure
		yōō	cute, few
e	elf, ten	ou	out, crowd
er	berry, care		
ē	even, meet	u	up, cut
		ʉr	fur, fern
i	is, hit		
ir	mirror, here	ə	a in ago
ī	ice, fire		e in agent
			e in father
ō	open, go		i in unity
ô	law, horn		o in collect
oi	oil, point		u in focus

CONSONANTS

SYMBOL	KEY WORDS	SYMBOL	KEY WORDS
b	bed, dub	v	vat, have
d	did, had	w	will, always
f	fall, off	y	yet, yard
g	get, dog	z	zebra, haze
h	he, ahead		
j	joy, jump	ch	chin, arch
k	kill, bake	ng	ring, singer
l	let, ball	sh	she, dash
m	met, trim	th	thin, truth
n	not, ton	*th*	then, father
p	put, tap	zh	s in pleasure
r	red, dear		
s	sell, pass		as in (ā'b'l)
t	top, hat		

Directions Read the respellings below. Notice the symbols in boldface print. Beside each respelling write the words from the pronunciation key that show how to pronounce that symbol. Then write the entry word for each respelling.

1. lēf   even, meet   leaf

2. round   _____   _____

3. *th*ose   _____   _____

4. burn   _____   _____

5. koil   _____   _____

6. pōol   _____   _____

7. sôrs   _____   _____

8. nōoz   _____   _____

9. äks   _____   _____

10. *th*er   _____   _____

Directions Use the pronunciation key on page 151 and accent marks to pronounce each respelling below. Then circle the syllable that is said with more stress.

Hint When a word has two or more syllables, one syllable is stressed, or accented, more than any other. In the dictionary, an accent mark (′) shows the syllable that is said with more stress.

1. rēd′ ing
2. trub′ ′l
3. man′ ij ər
4. mem′ ər ē
5. ri välv′
6. *th*er with′
7. dis tʉrb′
8. bil′ dər
9. un luk′ ē
10. ri fresh′ mənt
11. flɑun′ dər
12. kə rir′

Directions Use the pronunciation key on page 151 and accent marks to pronounce each respelling below. Then circle the word at the right that goes with that respelling.

1. sim′ p′l	simmer	single	simple
2. di zʉrv′	deserve	desert	dessert
3. pas′chər	pasture	patch	pastel
4. ə slēp′	assure	ashamed	asleep
5. baj	bug	badge	bus
6. thʉr′ ō	thereon	thought	thorough
7. jin′jər	jungle	ginger	garage
8. ik splō′ zhən	explain	exploring	explosion
9. so͞ot′ ə b′l	suited	suite	suitable
10. ga*th*′ ər iᵑg	gathering	gardenia	getaway

LESSON 76: Dictionary pronunciation key

Name _____

Directions For each group, match the word in boldface print with its respelling. Write the letter of the correct respelling beside the word. Use the pronunciation key below and accent marks as a guide.

a	fat	ī	bite, fire	ʉr	fur		**a** *in* ago
ā	ape	ō	go	ch	chin		**e** *in* agent
ä	car, lot	ô	law, horn	sh	she	ə =	**i** *in* unity
e	ten	oi	oil	th	thin		**o** *in* collect
er	care	oo	look	*th*	then		**u** *in* focus
ē	even	ōo	tool	zh	leisure		'*as in* ā'b'l
i	hit	ou	out	ŋ	ring		
ir	here	u	up				

_____ **1. anchor**   **a.** pri zurv

_____ **2. preserve**   **b.** jōo′ əl

_____ **3. hayfield**   **c.** drô ər

_____ **4. drawer**   **d.** hā fēld

_____ **5. jewel**   **e.** aŋ′ kər

_____ **1. second**   **a.** lik′ wid

_____ **2. liquid**   **b.** i nôr′ məs

_____ **3. enormous**   **c.** gur′g'l

_____ **4. loosen**   **d.** lōos′ 'n

_____ **5. gurgle**   **e.** sek′ ənd

Directions Use the pronunciation key and the accent marks to say the respellings. Fill in the circle next to the word that is the correct match for each respelling.

1. kär tōon′	○ carton ○ cartoon	2. grāz	○ graze ○ grass
3. kwīt	○ quite ○ quit	4. pouns	○ pounds ○ pounce
5. hwīn	○ whine ○ win	6. jok′ ē	○ joke ○ jockey
7. nōoz	○ nose ○ news	8. si ment′	○ comment ○ cement
9. hōz	○ hose ○ house	10. nīs	○ nice ○ niece

153

1.

rosebushes	erase
footstools	dispense
dispensing	footstool
knotted	rosebush
erasing	knot

2.

relieved	fly
equipping	ranger
rangers	knife
flies	equip
knives	relieve

3.

figuring	rebuild
carved	dimple
trophies	carve
rebuilding	figure
dimples	trophy

Directions   Read the paragraph below. Notice the numbered words in boldface print. On the lines below the paragraph, write each numbered word as you would find it as a dictionary entry word.

Among the earliest European **visitors** to North America was John Cabot. In 1497,
1

Cabot **landed** in North America. He is **believed** to be the first European to set foot on North
2   3

American soil since the Vikings, **hundreds** of years **earlier.** Cabot was in the service of the
4   5

English king and **claimed** the entire eastern coast of North America for England.
6

1. _____

2. _____

3. _____

4. _____

5. _____

6. _____

Name _____

Directions Read these dictionary entries. Decide which meaning of a word is used in each sentence below. Write the correct word and its definition number.

Rule When there is more than one meaning for an entry word, the different meanings are numbered. The most commonly used meaning is usually listed first.

ball (bôl) **n.** **1.** any round object; sphere. **2.** a game played with a ball, especially baseball. **3.** in baseball, a pitch that is not a strike and is not swung at by the batter.

band (band) **n.** **1.** a cord or wire, or a strip of some material, used to encircle something or to bind something together. **2.** a stripe of some different color or material. **3.** a group of musicians playing together.

interest (in′ trist or in′ tər ist) **n.** **1.** a feeling of wanting to know, learn, see, or take part in something. **2.** a share in something. **3.** money paid for the use of money; also, the rate at which it is paid.

office (ôf′ is) **n.** **1.** the place where a certain kind of business or work is carried on. **2.** an important position, job, or duty.

1. Eric has an _____ in music.

2. He joined the school _____ in seventh grade.

3. He ran for the _____ of band president.

4. He needed to buy a white uniform with a blue satin _____.

5. Eric used the _____ from his savings account.

6. The band was invited to perform at a _____ game in the stadium.

7. Eric picked up the tickets in the principal's _____.

8. The rubber _____ around the tickets broke!

155

Directions Read these entries. Decide which word to use to complete each sentence below. Write the entry word and its number on the line.

Hint Sometimes a word has a small raised number to the right of it. This indicates that there is another word pronounced and spelled the same way, but with a completely different meaning or origin.

hatch[1] (hach) **v.** to bring forth young birds, fish, turtles, etc. from eggs [Birds *hatch* their eggs by keeping them warm.]

hatch[2] (hach) **n.** an opening in the floor, especially of a ship, through which objects are passed [The cargo was loaded through the *hatch*.]

post[1] (pōst) **n.** a long, thick piece of wood, metal, etc. set upright for holding something up, as a building, sign, fence, etc.

post[2] (pōst) **n.** the place where a soldier, guard, etc. is on duty [The sentry walks a *post* just over the hill.]

rank[1] (raṅk) **n.** a row or line, as of soldiers placed side by side

rank[2] (raṅk) **adj.** having a strong, unpleasant taste or smell [*rank* fish].

stall[1] (stôl) **n.** a section for one animal in a stable.

stall[2] (stôl) **v.** to hold off by sly or clever means; delay by evading [He *stalled* for time.]

tire[1] (tīr) **v.** to make or become unable to go on because of a need for rest; exhaust [The hike *tired* me.]

tire[2] (tīr) **n.** a hoop of iron or rubber, or a rubber tube filled with air, fixed around the rim of a wheel to serve as a tread [The flat *tire* on the car made us late.]

1. Terry wrinkled his nose because the air smelled _____.

2. He hadn't cleaned Joker's _____ in two days.

3. Terry hitched him to a _____ while he did his chores.

4. Before he left the barn, he watched chicks _____.

5. On the way to school, he waved to a crossing guard at her _____.

6. Ten blocks from school, Terry's bicycle _____ went flat.

7. He was very _____ by the time the school bell rang.

LESSON 78: Homographs

Name _____

Directions   Now put your dictionary knowledge to work. Read these entries. Then follow the directions below.

contain (kən tān′) **v.**   **1.** to have in it; hold; enclose or include [This bottle *contains* cream.]   **2.** to hold back; control or restrain [Try to *contain* your anger.]

dominate (däm′ə nāt) **v.**   **1.** to control or rule; be most important or powerful [A desire to win *dominates* all her actions.]   **2.** to tower over; rise high above [These tall buildings *dominate* the city.]

efficient (ə fish′ ənt) **adj.** bringing about the result or effect wanted with the least waste of time, effort, or materials [an *efficient* method of production; an efficient manager].

mineral (min′ ər əl) **n.** a substance formed in the earth by nature; especially, a solid substance that was never animal or vegetable [Iron, granite, and salt are *minerals.*]

mint¹ (mint) **n.** a place where the government makes coins. **adj.** new; never used [a coin in *mint* condition]. **v.** to make into coins by stamping metal.

mint² (mint) **n.**   **1.** a plant with a pleasant smell whose leaves are used for flavoring, as peppermint and spearmint.   **2.** a piece of candy flavored with mint.

organize (ôr′ gə nīz) **v.**   **1.** to arrange or place according to a system [The library books are *organized* according to their subjects.]   **2.** to make part of a group, especially of a labor union [The coal miners were *organized.*]

region (rē′ jən) **n.**   **1.** a large stretch of land; area or district [an iron mining *region* of Minnesota].   **2.** any area, space, realm, etc. [the upper *regions* of the air].   **3.** a part of the body [the *region* of the liver].

tundra (tun′ drə or toon′ drə) **n.** a large, flat plain without trees in the arctic regions.

zinc (ziñgk) **n.** a bluish-white metal that is a chemical element. It is used to coat iron, and in making certain alloys, medicines, etc.

1.   Circle each word below that would come before the word **dominate** in alphabetical order.

door   dolly   dock   donkey

dormitory   dodge   dot   double

2.   Circle the guide words that would be on the same page as the word **region.**

restful/return   react/rebus   reason/remnant

3.   Write each word from the entries at the top that has only one syllable.

_____   _____

Directions   Write the number of the meaning of the word in boldface print that is used in each sentence below.

_____   **1.**   The pine tree in our front yard has grown quickly, and it now **dominates** the view from the window.

_____   **2.**   Jody added **mint** flavoring to the cookie mixture.

_____   **3.**   I felt a sharp pain in the lower **region** of my back.

157

Directions Suppose that the paragraphs below are part of a report you have just finished writing. Proofread the report. Circle each spelling mistake. Write the correction above each error. Use the dictionary entries on page 157 to check the words that are listed there.

Rule When you finish any piece of writing, carefully proofread what you have written. The dictionary is a helpful tool for proofreading.

Canada's Northern Region

Canada's Northern Rejin containes one of the world's largest and most valuable wilderness areas. It consists of two territories, the Yukon and the Northwest Territory, which have not yet been orgenized as provinces. The area stretches from the Great Lakes to the St. Lawrence River all the way to the Arctic.

The warmer, southern part of the Northern Region is dommniated by forests that support an important lumbering industry. To the north, the tundres supports only a few Native Americans. These people survive on a land that is frozen in winter and swampy in summer.

The greatest wealth of the area comes from meneral deposits of uranium, gold, iron, zink, copper, and lead. Transportation systems now being built will enable people to reach these deposits for efficiend development of the area.

General Rules

Short-Vowel Rule: If a word or syllable has only one vowel and it comes at the beginning or between two consonants, the vowel is usually short–**am, is, bag, fox**.

Long-Vowel Rule I: If a syllable has two vowels, the first vowel is usually long and the second vowel is silent–**rain, kite, cane, jeep, ray**.

Long-Vowel Rule II: If a word or syllable has one vowel and it comes at the end of the word or syllable, the vowel is usually long–**we, go, pony**.

Y as a Vowel Rule:
1) If **y** is the only vowel at the end of a one-syllable word, **y** has the sound of **long i–fly, by**.
2) If **y** is the only vowel at the end of a word of more than one syllable, **y** usually has the sound of **long e–silly, baby**.

Soft C and G Rule: When **c** or **g** is followed by **e, i,** or **y,** it is usually soft–**ice, city, change, gym**.

To make a word **plural**:
1) Usually just add **s–cats, dogs, kites**.
2) If a word ends in **x, z, ss, sh,** or **ch,** usually add **es–foxes, dresses, peaches**.
3) If a word ends in **y** preceded by a consonant, change the **y** to **i** and add **es–flies, fairies, babies**.
4) If a word ends in **f** or **fe,** usually change the **f** or **fe** to **v** and add **es–wolf/wolves, knife/knives**.
5) If a word ends in **o,** usually just add **s** to make the word plural. Some words are made plural by adding **es–potato/potatoes, tomato/tomatoes, hero/heroes**.
6) Some words change their vowel sound in the plural form–**man/men, tooth/teeth, mouse/mice**.

To add other suffixes:
1) When a short-vowel word ends in a single consonant, usually double the consonant before adding a suffix that begins with a vowel–**running, hummed, batter**.
2) When a word ends in silent **e,** drop the **e** before adding a suffix that begins with a vowel–**baking, taped, latest**.
3) When a word ends in **y** preceded by a consonant, change the **y** to **i** before adding a suffix other than **ing–cried, crying, happily, funnier, ponies, trying**.

To make a noun show **possession**:
1) Add **'s** to a singular noun–**dog's, James's, child's**.
2) Add an apostrophe only to a plural noun that ends in **s–boys', the Browns', babies'**.
3) Add **'s** to a plural noun that does not end in **s–mice's, children's, women's**.

To divide words into **syllables**:
1) A one-syllable word is never divided–**day, switch**.
2) Divide a compund word between the words that make up the compound word–**in-to, sun-shine**.
3) When a word has a suffix, divide the word between the base word and the suffix–**health-ful, kind-ly**.
4) When a word has a prefix, divide the word between the prefix and the base word–**dis-please, re-place**. Some prefixes have more than one syllable–**in-ter-change, o-ver-charge**.
5) When two or more consonants come between two vowels in a word, the word is usually divided between the first two consonants–**al-most, doc-tor**.
6) When a single consonant comes between two vowels in a word, the word is usually divided after the consonant if the first vowel is short–**drag-on, rob-in**.
7) When a single consonant comes between two vowels in a word, the word is usually divided before the consonant if the first vowel is long– **pi-lot, fa-mous**.
8) When a vowel is sounded alone in a word, the vowel is a syllable in itself–**u-nit, dis-o-bey**.
9) When two vowels come together in a word and are sounded separately, divide the word between the two vowels–**gi-ant, sci-ence**.
10) When a word ends in **le** preceded by a consonant, divide the word before that consonant–**cir-cle, nee-dle**.

Definitions

The **vowels** are **a, i, u, o, e,** and sometimes **y** (when it has the sound of **long i** or **long e**) and **w** (when it is part of a vowel digraph, as in **cow.**)

The **consonants** are all the remaining letters of the alphabet and usually **y** and **w.**

A **consonant blend** consists of two or more consonants sounded together so that each consonant can be heard–**black, train, swim, spring, fast, lamp.**

A **consonant digraph** consists of two consonants that together represent one sound–**when, thin, this, church, sheep, pack, know, white.**

A **vowel digraph** is an irregular double vowel that does not follow Long-Vowel Rule I–**school, book, bread, auto, yawn, eight.**

A **diphthong** consists of two vowels blended together to form a compound speech sound–**cloud, boy, oil, cow, new.**

A **compound word** is made from two or more smaller words–**doghouse (dog house), sandbox (sand box).**

A **contraction** is a short way to write two words as one. It is made by writing the two words together, leaving out one or more letters, and replacing the missing letters with an apostrophe (').

Synonyms are words that have the same or almost the same meaning.

Antonyms are words that are opposite or almost opposite in meaning.

Homonyms are words that sound alike but have different meanings and usually different spellings.

Homographs are words that are spelled the same, but have different meanings and different word backgrounds. Some homographs have different pronunciations.

A **base word** is a word to which a prefix or suffix may be added to form a new word–**printer, unpack, likely.**

A **root** is a word part to which a prefix or suffix may be added to form a new word–**introduction, prospector, reduce.**

A **suffix** is a word part that is added at the end of a base word to change the base word's meaning or the way it is used–**sprinter, darkness, helpful.**

A **prefix** is a word part that is added at the beginning of a base word to change the base word's meaning or form a new word–**recycle, unwrap, disappear.**